The 3rd & last
SECRET DIARY
OF JOHN MAJOR

Published in Great Britain
by Private Eye Productions Ltd
6 Carlisle Street, London W1V 5RG
in association with Corgi Books

ISBN 0 552 14281 6

Designed by Bridget Tisdall
Printed in England by
Ebenezer Baylis & Son Ltd, Worcester

Corgi Books are published by Transworld Publishers Ltd
61–63 Uxbridge Road, Ealing, London W5 5SA
in Australia by Transworld Publishers (Australia) Pty, Ltd
15–23 Helles Avenue, Moorebank, NSW 2170
and in New Zealand by Transworld Publishers (N.Z.) Ltd
3 William Pickering Drive, Albany, Auckland

2 4 6 8 10 9 7 5 3 1

Illustrated by
Caroline Holden

PRIVATE EYE • CORGI

MAJOR-BALL
BIROS
BUMPER VALUE
SEMI
STIFF
COVERS

JUNE

Monday

Today I began the great fight back to show everybody why I am the best man to be prime minister, and in no way as unpopular as everybody says I am. At breakfast this morning my wife Norman had left propped up against the toast rack a copy of the *Daily Telegraph* saying I am the most hated prime minister since William the Conqueror. This is quite an achievement for someone with only one O-Level, I think everyone would agree!

"Never mind," said Norman, as she was clearing away the plates. "At least there's one person who still loves you." "That is very kind of you, Norman," I said to her, preparing to give her an affectionate shake of the hand.

"Not me, John," she said, remembering my name. "I mean Sir Norma Fowler."

As it happened I had to meet Sir Norma that morning when we both spoke to a very successful rally of Conservative ladies, who as a joke had all come wearing orange rosettes saying "We Love Paddy". My speech, which had been written for me by my very clever new assistant Morris Norris, went down very well with the Conservative ladies, especially when I read out the bit which said: "Departing from prepared text you will ad lib as follows: Now is the time to be planting out the delphiniums. That is what I propose to do this weekend, and not sit around feeling depressed about losing some silly by-election. The only things which depress me are losing the football and losing the Test Match. And of course losing Newbury." I added that last bit in myself, to show that I am honest, but I don't think Mr Norris was very pleased, and he refused to talk to me in the car on the way home. But the Conservative ladies were very appreciative, and when I had finished my speech several of them clapped, including my wife Norman and Miss Hogg who had come along to make up the numbers.

Tuesday

I woke up this morning to hear a loud hooting from the street, and when I looked out of the window I saw my friend Sir Norma Fowler driving up in his Group 4 van. As it stopped, the back doors opened and several men in shirts with arrows on them ran off down the street laughing. Sir Norma came in the door, looking not inconsiderably white-faced, and shouting wildly about my ex-friend Norma Lamont who sadly had to be resigned. "Don't panic, prime minister, everything's under control. David Mellor has had lunch with Norma Lamont at a very expensive restaurant called La Tante Claire Latimer, and has fixed everything. Norma has given his solemn assurance that he will not stand up in the House of Commons and say that you are useless. He says he will show exactly the same loyalty to you as you showed to him."

I was greatly relieved to hear this and became much less depressed, which of course I am not.

Wednesday

Today was the day I had been really looking forward to, when I was going to finally show up what a hopeless leader of his party Mr Smith is. To begin with everything was going well, until I heard a familiar clanking of bottles. When I turned round I saw that Mr Lamont was squeezing into a seat behind me, carrying a Thresher's bag marked "Praed Street Comes Before A Fall", with a strangely flushed look on his face. Then he stood up and made a very peculiar speech, saying that the government was no good and had no idea what it was doing. Luckily it went down very badly. All the Labour MPs were laughing at him, and our side simply ignored him. Then it was my turn to point out that my job of being prime minister is a very difficult one indeed, and not everyone could do it. All the MPs on both sides shouted "Hear! Hear!" Mr Smith made a considerably pathetic reply, so much so that everyone laughed all the way through it. Then my new friend Mr Clarke made an absolutely brilliant speech, saying that the Labour Party should "shut up their faces" because they were "no bloody good". Afterwards, I heard several MPs say that Mr Clarke was "just the man we're looking for", which I thought was a great tribute to my judgement in choosing him to succeed Mr Lamont.

Thursday

As usual the papers have got it all wrong, saying "Can Major Survive After Lamont Attack?" What a very silly question, considering that I have just resigned him. I was much more impressed when I heard Sir Norma Fowler on Newsnight, Today, Call Nick Ross and the Classic FM 10 O'Clock British Steel Newsround slot, reminding everyone that it was me who won the election last year, and that Mr Lamont's speech had been "disloyal, dishonest, disreputable, discreditable" and a lot of other words beginning with "dis" which I had not heard of before, but which must have made Mr Lamont not inconsiderably discomfortable!

Friday

Mr Mates came round this morning and said he would like to give me one of his famous watches. "Oh," I said, "is this a gesture of support?" "No, Prime Minister," he said. "It is a leaving present, just in case you are thinking of going to Northern Cyprus and not coming back."

When I looked at the watch I saw that he had thoughtfully written on it: "Stop getting us down, you bugger."

Monday

I have decided to be in no way critical towards Norma Lamont for his disgraceful treachery to me. I will certainly not engage in public slanging matches which do neither of us any credit, even though I am entirely in the right. My decision was in no way affected by a strange fax from Norma with the message: "You lay off, matey, or I'll spill the beans."

Tuesday

At last we are out of the woods and Mrs Hogg assures me that the Government is back on course.

Mr Lilley, who is in charge of pensions and benefits, has come up with an excellent new idea for reducing the deficit (left by you-know-who!). He says we should reduce payments to invalids and people who are no longer capable of gainful employment.

"So we're cutting your salary, are we, John?" said Mr Clarke, the new Chancellor, with a nice smile. Everyone laughed, which is a sign that Norma Lamont is already forgotten.

Monday

At last things are beginning to look up. Oh yes. Not that things have been in any way looking down. Oh no. But Mr Clarke has made in my judgement a very fine speech to some businessmen in the City, setting out our new policy for the economy, i.e. we go for growth, we keep taxes down and we continue our war against inflation. This certainly shows a refreshing change from the bad old days of Mr Lamont, and his obsession with keeping inflation down, not putting up taxes and making silly speeches about growth.

I had made a plan to go to the Test Match at Lord's today, and my wife Norman had even made me one of her special packed lunches, i.e. an M&S Tuna Tikka Masala and Kumquat Danish Sandwich and an apple. She had not, however, included the customary Kit-Kat, which was not inconsiderably disappointing. But it didn't matter because Mr O'Donnell came in and told me I wasn't going to Lord's after all.

"It is not a good idea to be associated with defeat, failure and national humiliation," he said. Norman agreed, saying "No wonder the team doesn't want you there!" I think she has got the wrong end of the stick as per usual!

Tuesday

Once again the media are trying to tell me who I should have in my government. In this case it is Mr Mates who was a colonel in the army and a good friend of Mr Heseltine's. Everyone is saying that I should sack him just because he tried to interfere with the course of justice on behalf of someone who had given the Conservative Party a very considerable amount of money. Whatever the rights and wrongs of this business, I have decided to make it clear that in no circumstances whatever will I ask for the resignation of one of my most valued ministers.

When I told Sir Norma Fowler this, he gave me one of his panicky looks and said: "So you will be giving him the same 100% backing as you gave Mr Mellor and Mr Lamont?" "Exactly," I said firmly.

Wednesday

Very sadly Mr Mates has decided that, after a long and painful fax from me telling him that he has been sacked, he must resign. This is a serious blow, particularly to Mr Mates. But for the good of the government and the country as a whole, I have decided to accept his sacking. It is certainly tough at the top, though not so tough as it is just below the top!

When we were having our breakfast Norman said: "I see you have lost another of your Mates."

"I do not think that is amusing," I told her, "particularly as I have just read in the *Daily Telegraph* that Mr Heseltine has had a not inconsiderably serious heart attack in Venice, which is in Italy. That means that I have lost three ministers in a fortnight. It is true what Shakespeare said, that when bad things happen, they come in threes."

"Like Mates," said Norman, as she continued to munch her Brontosaurus Flakes. I was not exactly sure what she meant.

July

Thursday

Today I had to go to a place called Copenhagen for one of our many historic Euro-Summits. How different things are from the days when Mrs Thatcher used to go there and shout at our European partners! Now they shout at me.

First it was M. Delors who does not understand the first thing about how to make economies work. Then it was Mr Herr Kohl who has not a clue what to do about Bosnia. When we were having dinner he was so rude to me in German that I decided not to have coffee with him. That really put him in his place.

I cannot wait to get back to the House of Commons to tell them about my triumph.

Friday

It is not inconsiderably irritating when you have enjoyed a historic diplomatic triumph to find that everyone is only concerned with some quite silly and unimportant issue such as whether the Conservative Party should have accepted so much money at the last election from foreign crooks. I am glad to say that Sir Norma has come up with a brilliant defence. Every time the Labour Party asks about the millions of pounds we were given by the crooks, we all shout "Maxwell!" This always works, even when they say, "At least we declared it!"

Saturday

This silly secret fund business is continuing to cloud my triumph over Mr Herr Kohl and the coffee. Luckily Sir Norma has come up with a new brilliant idea, which is to say to the Labour Party: "We have to keep the names of all the people who give us money secret, or else people would know that they are crooks."

"By the way," I asked, "is it true, what it says in the *Guardian*, that we have taken millions of pounds in cash from the Arabs?"

"Yes," said Sir Norma, "it's all being guarded outside." He pointed through the window to a van which had written on the side "Group 4 — Mr Fowler Makes Exceedingly Safe Vans".

Sunday

After not an inconsiderable deliberation, I have decided that the Mates affair is now definitely over and we will not be discussing it any more.

Mr Mates rang me up to say he was working on his resignation speech. "I hope you're not offended by what I say," he said. "On the contrary," I said. "It is very kind of you to take the trouble to ring me up." It is a great pity that I have lost Mr Mates. He is certainly an officer and gentleman.

Later Mr Clinton rang me up to say that he had bombed Iraq for making an unsuccessful attempt to kill Mr Bush. "Did you kill Mr Hussein?" I asked. "No, we missed." "Then you are all square," I said, which was, in my judgement, a not inconsiderably astute observation.

Monday

The stories about my Press Officer Mr O'Donnell wanting to resign are quite untrue. I told him this when he came to see me this morning.

"Your job is to put good news about me into the papers," I said. "It wouldn't be good news if my own Press Officer wanted to leave me."

"Oh, I don't know," he replied, but I was having none of it. "You leave the thinking to me," I said decisively, "and tell the newspapers I have chosen a date for the Christchurch by-election." "When is that?" he asked. "I will just ask Sir Norma Fowler," I replied sternly.

Tuesday

I asked Sir Norma Fowler which day we would be most likely to win on, and he said, "How about February 30th?" How stupid he is sometimes. No wonder people keep on escaping from his vans! But to show how decisive I am, I have decided to choose the date myself. I opened my European Commission 1993 Executive Diary and saw that 29 July is Dairy Industry Day in Luxembourg. I thought this would be a considerably good omen and told Sir Norma to make all the necessary arrangements.

"We don't want this to be another Newbury," I told him in my sternest voice.

"I shouldn't worry about that, prime minister," he replied, "we won't do nearly that well."

Wednesday

I was very surprised this morning when the door opened and in burst Mr Heseltine pushing himself in a wheelchair. He looked very brown and fit and was wearing a T-shirt saying "I ♥ HEZZA".

"I thought you were connected to a drip?" I said.

"I am, John," he replied, "but I haven't seen you for weeks."

The effect of his medication obviously hasn't worn off yet! He very kindly brought me some grapes and one of those funny cards you give to people in hospital. On the outside it showed a dinosaur in a kilt, saying "I Hope You Get Better", and inside it said "You Couldn't Get Much Worse".

Mr Heseltine told me he had come in specially to see me, to reassure me that he was far from finished politically, and that he wanted people to know that he was still around for the day when the country needed him.

"That is very loyal of you, Michael," I said.

Thursday

Today I am in Japan for another very important meeting with Mr Gatt, the American trade minister, whom I have yet to meet. But it was very good to see so many of my old friends again, like Mr Clinton, Mr Herr Kohl and Mr Hurd.

On a personal note I was in no small measure gratified to note that of all the world leaders present I was the least most unpopular, with my latest poll rating of 14 percent. This is a good deal better than, say, Mr Clinton, who only has 3 percent, and the Japanese gentleman, who Mr Clarke told me is called Mr Han Din Til, whose rating is minus-30. I bet he's glad he's not having a by-election on July 29!

After several minutes of tough talking, we all agreed that we would tell the press we had pulled off an astonishing economic agreement, whereby everyone in the world was going to be £100 a week better off, there would be no more unemployment and we would all soon be much more popular with our voters.

Mr Clarke rather spoiled things by asking in a loud whisper what the actual agreement was about, but Mrs Clinton told him to put a sock in it.

Friday

Today we had a private meeting with the Japanese trade minister and we signed another very important and historic trade deal, whereby the Japanese agreed to sell us £800 billion worth of cars, videos and computer games, and in return they would buy a case of Scotch whisky and a selection of high-class teas in different coloured tins from Fortnum and Mason's. We called a press conference for the 11,000 journalists to announce this, but all they wanted to ask me about was the affair I didn't have with the cook. This was not inconsiderably irritating, despite the fact that here again I have won another historic victory, this time over the press — i.e. the *New Statesman* — which has agreed to pay me £1,000 for daring to suggest that I was not guilty of having an affair with our caterer. When I got back to our hotel I found a fax message from Sir Norma Fowler, offering to pick up my money in one of his Group 4 vans.

Saturday

On the plane home I read the new novel by my friend Jeffrey Archer. As the cover says, it is "a gripping tale of power and passion in high places". How suitable therefore that I should be reading it in an aeroplane! The story is certainly gripping. It is about a prime minister called James Colonel who finds himself the victim of a plot, when he is accused of having an affair with a beautiful caterer by a left-wing magazine. I'm afraid I found it entirely unconvincing. The Colonel character is so boring that he would never do anything as interesting as that.

Monday

Sir Norma Fowler has shown me a new by-election poll which puts our Party in third place behind Labour and the Social Democrats. Sir Norma said this was good news as, from now on, things could only get better.

"All the Party's big guns will turn out to help win the seat," he said. "Except Mr Heseltine and most of the others who will be on holiday."

"What about Mr Hurd?" I asked him, since Mr Hurd is well known as a vote-getter. "No," said Sir Norma. "I asked him if he would go to Christchurch and he said 'No, Balliol is a much better college'." Sometimes I am not sure what Mr Hurd means.

I told Mr Fowler not to worry about Christchurch because after my triumph with Mr Gatt I would be terrifically popular with the voters. "I have secured Jobs for the Future," I told him. "But not for everyone," he said giving me a funny look. He then had to go to see the Police because one of his vans had been stolen.

Sunday

Today for the first time ever I have had to miss the social highlight of the year — my friend Lord Archer's garden party. Norman had to go on her own and said she met lots of famous people, like Mr Gummer and the man who plays Inspector Morse on the television (I think). I was far too busy preparing my historic speech which will win over the Tory rebels once and for all. "Back me or I stay," that will be my theme.

Monday

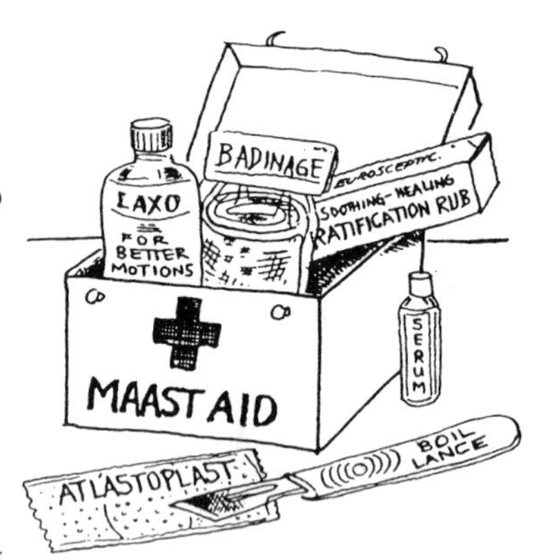

Lord Rees-Mogg has in no small measure got into my little black book again. He is going to the courts to get the judges to say that my Maastricht Treaty is illegal. This is totally undemocratic, as our lawyers have already assured me that it is perfectly legal even if Parliament rejects it!

The Treaty anyway now has the Royal Assent, which means that the Queen must have said she likes it. (This is another triumph for myself by the way as I promised her that her head would still appear on the European stamps.)

To celebrate this not inconsiderably satisfactory development I went out with a few photographers to the shop where my ex-friend Mr Mellor used to go and bought a CD. I chose one of a skiffle group called "Lonnie Donegan at 80". No one can say now that I am out of touch! Oh no.

Wednesday

I am very glad to say that Mr Lamont has turned over a new leaf and has quite put his old bitterness behind him. Today he got up in the House of Commons and congratulated Mr Clarke on the fact that all his new policies were working so quickly. Mr Lamont pointed out that since he had stopped being Chancellor, the recession had immediately come to an end and Britain was now having an economic boom thanks entirely to Mr Clarke.

Unfortunately a lot of MPs laughed at Mr Lamont for saying this, but he took it in good heart and smiled broadly back. When I got home my wife Norman was waiting up for me, even though it was long after half-past-eight.

"Hullo, John," she said, "you're a head at last."

"That is very perceptive of you," I said, "everyone else thinks that I am going to lose over Maastricht."

She then explained that she had been invited to an art gallery where there was a bust of me! It shows I am getting quite famous!

"What is the statue like?" I asked her.

"Well," she replied, handing me an individual portion of M&S's Salmon and Coriander Fish Cake Provençal, "the critics thought it was a bit dull, grey and lifeless, but I thought it looked just like you."

Thursday

This was the most historic of my many historic days recently. And I am in no small measure furious at the way some of my party have behaved. They are Bastards. I would not say this to anyone, but in the privacy of my own diary I have to say that they are not inconsiderable Bastards. And disloyal Bastards as well.

I spent the whole day in the Commons being nice to them and my friend Sir Norma Fowler backed me up by telling them that he would put them in one of his prisons if they didn't vote for my Maastricht Treaty. But they all laughed. Fortunately there were some very nice Irishmen called the Ulster Unionists who said that they would support me. "There will be no deal with you," I said. "OK," they agreed, and added, "and no deal with Dublin." They gave me a big wink and said: "It's a deal."

Usually these Irishmen are against Europe but today they were for it. Just as usually Labour are for Europe but today they are against it. It is all very confusing.

As I said in my very well received indeed speech: "Everyone except us is voting the opposite way to what they believe in." "That's because you don't believe in anything," shouted someone who can only be described as a Bastard. Then we had a vote and some of the people who I now refer to as Bastards went through the wrong door marked "No" instead of the one marked "Aye". The score was: US 316 all out; THEM 324. The other side all started cheering as if they had won.

But they hadn't. Oh no. At our regular routine Emergency Cabinet Meeting in the middle of the night, as Mr Waldegrave was passing round the Horlicks, I had a brilliant idea. "Mr Hurd," I said. "What shall we do next?"

Mr Hurd then handed me a new motion to vote on tomorrow called a vote of confidence. It read:

"This House supports Mr Major because otherwise there will be an election and we'll all lose our jobs because he is so useless."

Friday

It worked. The House of Commons finally came to their senses and voted for my brilliant handling of the Maastricht Treaty.

Mr O'Donnell was jubilant. "We can now draw a line under Maastricht," he said, "and move forward to lose the Christchurch by-election." I agreed. We shall certainly hear no more of the Bastards or rebels, as they used to be known.

Sunday

I cannot believe it. I thought we had drawn a line under this. The newspapers are suggesting that I have called the rebels Bastards just because I said so to a television reporter! "What Bastards!" I said to my wife Norman in bed. "It was all off the record." "Which record was that?" she asked. "Was it your Lonnie Donegan one?" She seems to be in an inappropriately good mood at the moment and keeps singing "Goodbye Downing Street" cheerfully under her breath.

MEMO: The following are in my judgement Bastards and are now in my special Black Book of Bastards.

1) Edward Heath. How dare he criticise my leadership? He was a total failure who got us into Europe in the first place.

2) Mrs Thatcher. Ditto. Her period of office was a disaster for this country. *Not* a Golden Age at all as some of these Bastards think.

3) All the Bastards who think that Thatcher's was a Golden Age. Including: a) Mr Portfolio; b) Mr Howard; c) Mr Redwood; d) Mr Lilley; e) Lots of other Bastards as well.

It would be easy to sack these people. That would be the cowardly route. It is much braver not to sack them in case they cause trouble.

Look what happened with Norma Lamont and Mr Mates!

Monday

I called Mr O'Donnell round to No. 10 today to demand an apology from the BBC for leaking my remarks about Bastards. "It must have been them," I said, "because they have it in for me."

"They are not the only ones, Prime Minister," he said. "But anyway 'Bastardgate' has been a great success for you. It shows that you are tough-talking and aren't frightened to say what you think. The whole thing might make you less unpopular, like when you didn't have an affair with the cook." This was very encouraging.

"Perhaps I should go to Christchurch and tell the voters that if they don't vote for me they are Bastards," I suggested.

Mr O'Donnell thought this was a brilliant idea, but

unfortunately he had arranged for me to be in Siberia this week on a very important trade mission.

Friday

Today is a very unhistoric day. A man called Mr Hayward has lost the Christchurch by-election, and unfortunately he was standing for the Conservatives. But fortunately Sir Norma Fowler was able to explain to me on Newsnight that in fact we had won a great victory. Firstly everyone had been predicting that the swing against us would be 35 percent, and it was only 34.8 percent. And secondly we completely thrashed the Labour Party, who even lost their deposit. They really are useless! No wonder nobody votes for them. Besides we have now drawn a line under this, as we have successfully done under Maastricht, Newbury and the so-called Bastardgate. All these now have lines drawn under them, with my special new set of coloured biros which I bought at Ryman's — with free refills, which I shall definitely need as there are so many things to draw lines under these days!

August

Saturday

Imagine how not inconsiderably annoying it was to see that the papers this morning were still full of Bastardgate, Maastricht and Christchurch. Don't they realise that a line has been drawn under all three? Sometimes the papers make themselves look very stupid by being so out of touch with things that have had a line drawn under them.

As she read the stories out to me, my wife Norman said: "I am very shocked by some of these words you have been using to Mr Brunson."

"Oh," I replied, with no small measure of embarrassment, "what words are those?"

She laughed and said: " 'Decision', 'action', 'leadership'." She then went off to Boots to buy some things for our holiday, including some special sun cream called "Factor 94" which she said would stop me going red — "particularly after the next by-election result". I had no idea what she meant.

Monday

Entirely as I predicted, the ERM has collapsed. I called in Mr O'Donnell and told him to inform the press that this only showed I had been completely right all along. " 'PM Says — I Told You So' — that is the headline I want to read tomorrow."

Mr O'Donnell, in my judgement rather rudely, said, "Yes, you told them on 15 September last year that 'we will never leave the ERM and it is absolutely vital to Britain's economic future'."

I told him that I had drawn a line under that speech as well.

Tuesday

Mr Lamont is trying to claim credit for Britain leaving the ERM. What utter rubbish. It was my idea to leave it, just as it was my idea to go back in again when the time was right. However that does not change the fact that I was right to leave the ERM when the Germans forced me to.

Another thing about the collapse of the ERM is that it completely shows up how wrong the so-called Euro-rebels are. They claim that Europe won't work whereas the ERM shows that we Europeans can all agree to draw a line under something when it doesn't work. In a spirit of mutual co-operation. Oh yes.

Wednesday

I am afraid that the lady whose name I cannot mention has really gone too far this time. She has been talking to television reporters, showing yet again her total lack of judgement. She has described several members of *her* Cabinet as "Bastards" for betraying her, and she has not even had the courage to name them. This only shows, what I have always said, that she should never have been prime minister.

Thursday

Mr O'Donnell was very excited and told me that I had been asked to write a column for the *News of the World*. This is a very important paper read by millions of people.

"I am very flattered but I am a busy man and I do not have the time to write a column..."

"You already have," he said, producing some typewritten sheets from his briefcase.

I must admit it was very good and I agreed with nearly all of it. For example, I say:

"Who says Britain is finished? Not me! Oh no! Look at our export figures. They speak for themselves. And didn't Nigel Mansell do well in that race? He is British. So am I. Three cheers for us."

It was so good I said to Mr O'Donnell: "I could do this every week. Even when I am on holiday."

Friday

Today I was very busy indeed going to the Test Match and being photographed. England have a new captain but are still losing. This shows there is no point in changing the man at the top just because the newspapers say he is no good.

Saturday

Today we went to Gatwick airport, where we joined up with our Suntour for the flight to a country called Algarvia, I think. Anyway, it is on the Mediterranean and is very hot. On the plane I read the new novel by my friend Jeffrey Archer. It starts very grippingly by describing the prime minister of England, James Colonel, sitting on a plane to Portugal, reading a brilliant new novel by the brilliant novelist Godfrey Bowman. In the book Colonel suddenly realises that he has made a terrible mess of running the country, and decides that, as the plane lands, he will ring up the Queen and tell her to appoint Godfrey Bowman as prime minister instead of him (not one of Jeffrey's best, I'm afraid).

When we arrived at our time-share I told Norman what a relief it was to get completely away from all the nasty things they have been saying about me in the newspapers. Now I can just relax by the pool and read the papers which Sir Robin Butler has arranged to have flown out to me every day.

Monday

I am really enjoying our holiday in Algarvia, which is near Portugal. It is very hot, but if you jump into the pool you are soon quite cool again! Unfortunately there is no pool in this particular villa, which is odd since my friend Jeffrey distinctly assured me that all the houses in Algarvia have pools. "Only an idiot", he said, "would take a villa without a pool." Perhaps I should ring my friend Mr Gummer who knows some business people who put pools in for free!

This morning, our cook Latima (who is, in my judgement, quite pretty!) came out shouting "Señor Hurd, Señor Hurd!" "No," I told her, "I am Señor Major, the prime minister of England. Señor Hurd, he in London, running country." I spoke very slowly, like Mr Heath does when he is speaking French. It worked, because she immediately said: "With great respect, Señor Major, what I meant was that your friend Señor Hurd is on the telephone from London and wishes to speak to you urgently."

Mr Hurd (who is not señor at all) told me that I had to come home at once as there was a terrific opportunity to boost my popularity. "Surely," said Norman, "you would best achieve that by staying here and keeping out of the way?" As so often, she had rather missed the point.

Tuesday

When I arrived back in London I found a top-level meeting about Bosnia taking place around the television in my office. "Look," said Mr Hurd, pointing to a picture of a little girl lying in bed in hospital, "that is Irma. All the papers are going on about her. They are all screaming for us to do something."

"No," I explained to him in my firm voice. "My policy on Bosnia is not to do anything. This is a civil war, and nothing to do with us. I was told that by a very senior member of the Government."

"Yes," said Mr Hurd, "it was me — and now I'm telling you something else."

Mr O'Donnell then took over the meeting and outlined what he called his secret plan for winning the next election, "Operation War Tot".

"I have got the media ready," he went on. "All you have to do is press the button and tomorrow's headlines will read 'Caring John Saves Toddler Irma', 'Little Irma — She's Safe And Sound Thanks To Decisive Courageous Major', and 'PM's Popularity Soars As Flyaway Babe Jets In'."

"Isn't this something of a U-turn in our policy?" I asked.

Mr Hurd gave me one of his very special, toffee-nosed looks and said: "No, prime minister, our *policy* is just the same. This is just a PR stunt."

"Oh," I said, "that's alright then. I'd hate people to think we have no principles."

Wednesday

Mr Hurd and Mr O'Donnell's idea has worked brilliantly. All the headlines are just as they predicted, and my popularity is already back above 10 per cent! "Another five Irma's," I told Mr Hurd, "and we are home."

"Unlike all those 10 million refugees in the former Yugoslavia," chipped in Mr Waldegrave somewhat unhelpfully, as he brought in the mid-morning tray of our new beverage, Mrs Bottomley's Nicotine-Free Tea.

Thursday

Today we had another very important meeting of my new "War Tot Cabinet". I suggested that we should find some more children who could be flown in to be on News At Ten with Mr Barbados. But Mr Hurd butted in to say: "Unfortunately, prime minister, there is a slight problem. We have been told by the United Nations that if we want any more war victims they have to include some adults."

"Why is that a problem?" I interposed. "We don't have to show the adults on television, do we?" I am getting very media-wise these days, as you can see, especially after writing my brilliant column in the *News of the World*! But Mr Howard, who is the new Home Secretary, explained that any adults coming in would require visas, immigration documentation and work permits from the Home Office, which he could not possibly give them. In those circumstances, he said, he would have no alternative but to send round the police to deport them back to Sarajevo.

"This is typical of the UN," I said. "After all we have done to help, they tie us up in red tape."

It is time the UN had the Citizen's Charter. I must remind Mr Waldegrave to write a letter to Mr Boutros Boutros Ghali. Even his name has to be in duplicate, which shows how typically wasteful the UN is. Imagine if I was called John John Major! People would not take me seriously.

Friday

Mr Howard has got some new ideas to make prisons more unpleasant. "Surely," I asked him in my special inquiry voice, "the prisoners will try and escape?"

"Yes," he said, "but we will have extra security provided by Sir Norma Fowler's Group 4." Mr Waldegrave gave him a funny look as he cleared away the cups of Options Lo-Fat chocolate drink.

Talking of Sir Norma, people are saying that I should replace him as Party chairman and have Mr Heseltine instead. My wife Norman was unsure: "We do not want any more heart attacks when he does one of his brilliant speeches."

"But Mr Heseltine is fully recovered," I countered.

"It's not him I was thinking about," she said.

Monday

I am back on holiday in Algarvia. Oh yes. No one can accuse me of not relaxing! I went for a short walk into the village this morning to buy some insect repellant, as my wife Norman and I have been bothered by the mosquitoes. I did not know the Algarvian word for mosquito, but I pointed out one of my bites to the shopkeeper and made a whining noise. "Ah," he said, "Señor Kenneth Baker — grande Bastardo!" I was in no small measure puzzled by this display of Algarvian banter, until he brought out a copy of the *Indipendente do Algarve*, which had a big headline saying "Majore E Judas Dica Baker — Ritorno di Maggie Probabile". I realised at once that I was so relaxed that I could now return home immediately.

Tuesday

It seems that a very grave crisis has arisen while I was leaving Mr Hurd to run the country. Mr Baker, who in my judgement always had a not inconsiderably irritating smile, has written an article in the *Sunday Times* saying that I invented a toothache so that I would not have to support Mrs Thatcher in the leadership contest. As I told the Cabinet at an emergency session: "It is completely untrue that I did not have toothache. My diaries will prove this when they are published after I have stopped being prime minister."

"Oh," said Mr Waldegrave, as he handed round a plate of the new Chocolate Bungee-Jumpers, "so we'll all be reading about it at Christmas." Everyone laughed at Mr Waldegrave, who had clearly got the wrong end of the stick as usual. But then I put on my serious voice and asked my new friend Mr Clarke: "What can I do about this terrible smear?"

"If I was you, prime minister, which I probably soon will be, I would lie low for a few weeks and pretend you've got a toothache."

September

Wednesday

An even graver crisis is now confronting the nation. In spite of my triumph in saving the News at Ten, the ITV people are going to move it to half-past-six after all. You cannot do this to a national institution. Imagine if I was to move from Number 10 to Number Half-past-six — no one would take me seriously. I told Miss Hogg to send one of my famous angry faxes to the ITV bosses, saying that I was not inconsiderably displeased. It must have made a great impact, because I was later told that they had put it up on the notice board with the words "Stupid Bastard" written on it. Obviously that is what they thought of whoever had made such a silly decision.

Thursday

At our daily emergency Cabinet meeting we discussed all these rumours in the newspapers about the Cabinet being split on tax. I said there was no split, and Mr Clarke said there was. I am not sure he is my friend after all. "I gave the nation a solemn promise that we would not raise taxes," I said. "Well, that's all right," said Mr Clarke. "Everyone will be expecting you to put them up." In my judgement this was a very silly thing to say, and shows that Mr Clarke has not got the qualities of a prime minister, as all the uninformed people in the media keep saying.

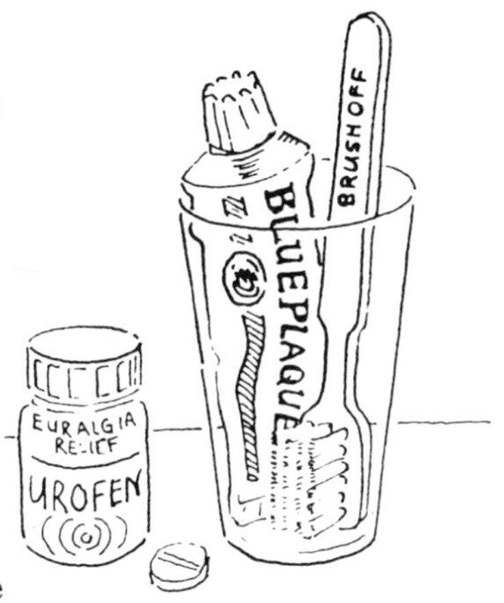

Friday

I was woken up this morning by a phone call from my friend Sir Norma Fowler. "Prime Minister," he said. "I have given up my non-executive job as a director of Group 4 to spend more time with you. And if they tell you that Group 4 has sacked me because I might stop them winning all the contracts to build the new private prisons, I want you to know that it's a complete lie."

"I perfectly understand, Norma," I said. "But I think resigning is a bit drastic. Couldn't you just pretend you had a toothache when the bids came up?"

Saturday

This morning I got a call from my former friend Norma Lamont. He wanted me to be the first to know that he has got a new non-executive job. "Does that mean they don't pay you?" I asked. "No, it means I don't have to work — and I get paid more than you," he said, and the phone went dead.

When Miss Hogg came in, I said: "Did you know that Mr Lamont has got a new job in the City?" "Of course I did," she said. "We fixed it up." "But why should a bank take on someone who doesn't know the first thing about money?" I asked. "Because if they didn't we wouldn't give them any more privatisation contracts," she said. "But why should we want them to help Mr Lamont?" I asked. "Because it's the only way to make sure he keeps his mouth shut during the Party conference," she explained. I am certainly very lucky to have such a clever woman as Miss Hogg around to make sure that my Government runs so smoothly.

Monday

I really am famous. A whole book has been written about me! It is by Penny Junor and it says I am an Enigma! I told this to my wife Norman at breakfast who said: "Well, that is a variation." I had no idea what she was talking about.

It says in the book that I will only give up being prime minister when I choose and I will not be forced out. This is quite right and shows what a good journalist Miss Junor is. Oh yes. I remember telling her: "When the time comes for me to go, I will stay on."

Saturday

Today I went in my helicopter to a place Mr O'Donnell called "the West Country". But when we arrived I found it was not a country at all, it was part of England. Mr O'Donnell explained that this was a "morale boosting tour" for me to meet my supporters. When we arrived at the hall, there were only two people there, which is not a considerable number of supporters in my judgement.

Mr O'Donnell was not unduly disappointed. "We invited all the Conservatives in Somerset to meet you," he said, "but the other couple are away on holiday."

I had a very interesting and useful exchange of views with the two stalwart Conservatives, who were both as it happened lifelong Chairmen of Tory Associations, and I was very gratified when they said that they were still hoping that they would be able to give me their support at the next election. They were not in the slightest bit worried about the tax that my friend Mr Kenneth Clarke is going to put on old people's heating bills. "We're going to keep the Aga going on old copies of your Manifesto," one of them said, "the one where you promised never to put up VAT."

Sunday

Today I have had a brilliant idea! I read an article in the *Sunday Times* saying that we never export anything to Japan, so I decided all on my own that I would fly to Tokyo and tell the Japanese to "buy British". I also had the brilliant idea of taking six students on the plane with me, so that they could write articles about me in their school magazines. This is better press than Mr O'Donnell ever got me! I am doing without advisers from now on, because they only come up with silly PR stunts which make me look ridiculous.

When I arrived I was allowed to meet the Japanese prime minister, who apologised that he was so busy, but he was very unpopular at the moment, his economy was in trouble and he was just about to leave on a morale-boosting tour of Japan. I felt not inconsiderably sorry for him being in such a mess. But I told him firmly that it was high time the Japanese bought more goods made in Britain. "Like what?" he asked, holding his sides and laughing, which the interpreter explained is an ancient Japanese gesture of respect.

After I had thought for a while, one of the schoolchildren, who were filming my historic meeting on video, passed me a note reading "Nissan cars are made in Newcastle". I immediately repeated this to the prime minister, who laughed uproariously and gave me a traditional samurai sword as a present. "It is called hara-kiri," he said. "You will find it very useful."

Monday

Today I have made another decision all on my own, without consulting either Mr O'Donnell or Miss Hogg. So much for my critics who say I cannot think for myself! I decided to fly to Monte Carlo (which is not in this country, although I am not exactly sure which country it is in!) to throw my full weight behind Manchester's bid to have the Olympic Games. I can't wait to

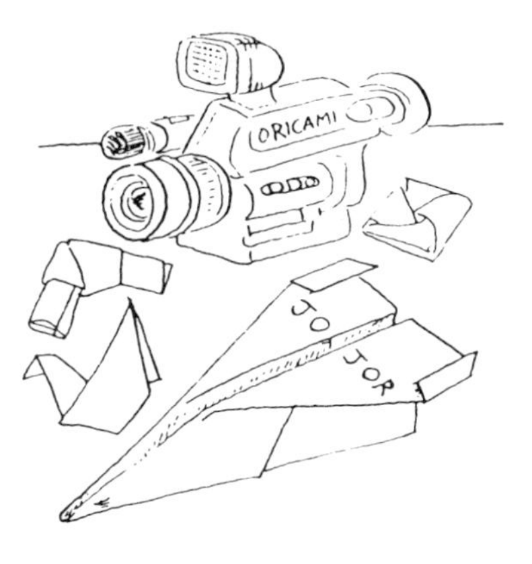

see all my advisers' faces when they see headlines reading "Manchester Wins Gold Thanks To PM's Brilliant Intervention".

When I arrived at the hotel, the Manchester officials were suitably surprised. "Good grief," they exclaimed, "look who's here. There's no doubt who'll win it now. Peking here we come!" I did not fully understand this, but I assumed that they were planning to go to a local Chinese restaurant to celebrate.

Tuesday

Today I have been on another of my brilliant morale-boosting flying visits. Only this time I did not have to take a plane, because I had gone to lend my support to our great chess player Mr Short (a Conservative supporter, by the way!) who is on his way to winning the world championship against the Russians. My wife Norman asked me why I wanted to be associated with "that silly little man with glasses who keeps losing". I took no notice of this advice (or indeed any other — oh no!) and I was very pleased when I arrived at the theatre to find that Mr Short was doing extremely well. He had come second in almost every game.

Mr Hurd has been trying to copy my Olympic Games idea! He has told everyone that China should not stage the Games because of their human rights record. I have to agree. It's all right to let them run Hong Kong but not something important like the Olympics.

Wednesday

The papers (which I never read) are still saying that my Cabinet is split over taxes. This is ridiculous and shows how little they know about what is going on. My friend Mr Clarke has apparently made a speech saying that he intends to put up taxes and keep benefits the same. Other people in the Cabinet say that he should keep taxes the same and cut down on the benefits. So where is this split they are all talking about? There must be some considerably unintelligent people working in the newspapers, who've probably got too many 'O' levels for their own good!

Memo to self: I am beginning to get in no small measure mildly furious about the way Mr Clarke is going round making speeches about all our policies. Anybody would think he is Prime Minister.

Thursday

I am beginning to think that my ex-friend Norma Lamont may be my friend again after all. He has written very nice articles in all the newspapers this morning saying that "with firm, decisive leadership, Britain can lead the world". This is a very generous tribute to my leadership skills which I particularly appreciate in view of the sad way in which I had to resign him. At last the newspapers are recognising all that I have done for Britain since I led us out of the ERM and into the recovery which is very much here. Oh yes, whatever the newspapers say. This is in my judgement a very good omen for our Party conference next month.

Friday

Norma Lamont is definitely my ex-friend again. He has now attacked me on television and even had the nerve to say that he supported me!

I have got a secret new book now to go with my secret "Bastards" book. It is called "Devils" and on the first page is Mr Lamont, who is also in the "Bastards" book as well. There are no fixed rules, but in certain circumstances a person, i.e. Mr Lamont, can be in both books, oh yes. There is also an ultra-secret "Loonies" book, which I showed to my wife Norma. "Why has it got your name on the front?" she asked, but did not wait for a reply. The first entry is Sir Richard Body, who is an MP who is challenging my leadership. "How dare he?" I asked our regular crisis Cabinet meeting. "He has no experience of being Prime Minister and would obviously make a terrible mess of it." "Sounds familiar," said Mr Waldegrave, as he brought in a hat with a lot of names in it. "This is not tea," I said.

Poor Mr Waldegrave! He is clearly cracking up and will soon find himself in the "Loonies Book".

Saturday

I have made it clear that I will not discuss the so-called Leadership Crisis which is not a crisis at all in any terms whatsoever in my judgement. This is a closed subject.

Sunday

My piece in the *Sunday Telegraph* on the leadership crisis

makes it clear that I am taking a tough line against so-called "Stalking Horses". My message to all MPs is clear and will definitely rally the party around me: "Back me or I stay." It could not be clearer than that. Oh no.

Monday

These are indeed historic times! Today in my lunch hour I had to go to Ryman's to buy another notebook, to go with my "Loonies", "Bastards" and "Devils" books, making four in all. This one is called my "Apples Short of a Picnic" book, after a brilliant phrase I came up with in Japan, or was it Manchester? No, I tell a lie, it was Malaya, a country I shall not be going back to again. Oh no. In fact, it is the first country to get into the "Bastards" book (under "M", which includes several other "M"s I don't mention!). This was the country where the prime minister insulted me in his speech of welcome by saying I had done nothing about Bosnia. Of course I did something about Bosnia. I took Mr Hurd's advice, which was to do nothing. Which is obviously something in my book! (Not my "Apples Short of a Picnic" book of course, but another one, which I must remember to go to Ryman's tomorrow to purchase!) And besides, what had the Malayans done about Bosnia, I should like to know? When I was in Bosnia last year there were several Malayans short of a picnic, I can tell you!

Tuesday

Today at breakfast, which was Semi-Skimmed Apple Juice plus Sainsbury's Picnic-style Muesli, my wife Norman asked me: "John, what do you mean when you keep saying someone 'is a few apples short of a picnic'?" I explained to her in my special humorous voice (which I have been practising for the jokes in my very important conference speech next week): "Surely it is obvious. People who criticise me are like someone who goes on a picnic but forgets to take enough apples."

She replied, somewhat

unnecessarily in my judgement: "In that case you should say that it is the *picnic* which is short of *apples*." Sometimes I think it is true that women have no sense of humour, except of course Mrs Bottomley who always laughs at my jokes in our Cabinet meetings.

Wednesday

I am becoming a famous journalist as well as being prime minister! Following my brilliant column in the *News of the World*, Mr O'Donnell tells me I have written an article in the *Economist* which everyone is talking about! I read it with great interest, and agreed with all of it, except the bits about Europe, which I thought were a bit negative. I was proved right, as usual, when Mr Delors appeared on television at lunchtime saying that I was "yesterday's man". I have immediately sent a not inconsiderably stern reply to Mr Delors which goes as follows:

Chers M. Delors,

Comment ça va? Je ne suis pas l'homme de hier.
Je suis l'homme d'aujourd'hui et l'homme du future,
en mon jugement. Oh oui. C'est vous, monsieur,
qui est l'homme d'hier.

Votre sincèrement,
Jean Majeur.

P.S. Votre nom est maintenant en toutes mes livres,
i.e. la livre de "Bâtardes", de "Loonies", de "Diables",
et meme le "Plusieurs de pommes bref d'un picnique"
livre. Prenez garde.

This letter which Miss Hogg helped me with, because she got French 'O' level, should certainly put Mr Delors in his place. He is just a faceless bureaucrat with glasses and no ideas, in my judgement. How he has got to the top I cannot imagine.

Thursday

Mr Smith has made a very poor showing at his Party conference. It is sad to see a leader who is so unpopular that even his closest colleagues, like his Number Two, Mrs Beckett, will not support him publicly. It would be rather like my own Number Two Mr Clarke going round saying that my government was in a terrible hole. Mr Smith's big speech was a complete flop. The only thing anybody enjoyed was all the silly jokes he made about me.

It was just the same with Mr Ashdown, who read out a silly poem about how I "wasn't there". Of course I wasn't there. I had gone to Tokyo. Mr Ashdown is clearly two party conferences short of an apple! As I said to the Cabinet: "It is all very easy to make fun of me just to get a few cheap laughs." They all agreed, which shows that there are no splits in our Party, oh no!

My speech next week is going to be the most important of my career, Mr O'Donnell tells me. I have told my Chief Speech Writer, Mr Morris Norris, that my main theme should be the need for more toilets on the M25. "But, prime minister, we did that last year," he said. "I know," I told him, "and it was a great success. That is why I must do it again."

I also suggested some jokes about Mr Smith, viz. that he must be "a few bananas short of an orange, and the Labour Party itself is short of a leader". Mr Norris was clearly very amused, but said that he would have to "give them a bit of a spin" before they could be used. He also had another idea. "Why don't you try a few jokes about yourself, prime minister? It worked brilliantly for Smith and Ashdown." Tonight another name has gone into my book.

October

Friday

I stayed up nearly all night working on my historic conference speech. I am writing it myself, since you cannot trust anyone nowadays, not even Miss Hogg and Mr O'Donnell, who are very near to being put in several of my books. So far the speech, which is all my own work, reads:

"Ladies and gentlemen. John Smith is a Bastard."

This evening I will do some more work on it.

Saturday

Mr Clarke tells me, on the television, that he is planning very savage cuts indeed to deal with government spending. "There are faceless men sitting at Government desks fiddling with their biros and writing rubbish in their notebooks. They are in for a shock."

This is very good indeed. I rang up Mr Clarke to congratulate him. "Yes," he said, "no one is safe. After the conference there will be blood on the carpet." Perhaps he is my friend after all.

Sunday

Believe it or not, someone else might be becoming my friend after all! The woman I never mention may have to be crossed out of my books.

She has announced that she is coming to the Conference to make it clear she supports me! I told the Cabinet this excellent news before we got in the Group 4 coach to the Conference in

Bournemouth which Sir Norma's old friends had kindly laid on. I told them Mrs Thatcher wants to change the rules about the Conservative leadership — "so some idiot can't get in by mistake". My colleagues all laughed. "And, what's more," I said, "she has agreed to raise funds for the Party at fêtes and the like."

"Perhaps she could run the White Elephant stall," said Mr Waldegrave, who has taken to wearing a gown and mortarboard in meetings. "Or is that *your* department?" Everyone laughed again. We are certainly in high spirits for the Conference. Oh yes.

Friday

Today I made what my wife Norman said was the best speech I have ever made in my life! Even I have to admit that in my own judgement it was a triumph.

I opened with a brilliant joke that was specially written for me by my new speechwriter Mr Morris Norris. This is how it went: "Everybody is writing their memoirs." (This, by the way, was a coded attack on Mrs Thatcher!) "But," I went on, "I want you all to know that I have no intention of writing my memoirs. Certainly not yet at any rate!" Everyone laughed, especially when Mr O'Donnell held up a board with the word "Laugh" written on it in big letters.

But that was not the only joke I told. Oh no. During the section when I attacked the way education has got much worse in the past 14 years, I pointed out that it is now illegal to read Shakespeare in schools. Shakespeare, my favourite author, can you believe it? I put on my special funny Cockney voice and said, "Fings ain't what they used to be." Everyone laughed again, especially when Mr O'Donnell held up another board saying "This bit is meant to be funny as well".

But I also made some very serious points in my speech, which went on for a very considerable period of time. The main point that I wanted to make was that the country is in a terrible state these days, due to the Labour Government in the Sixties, and that what we need is a return to Conservatism. "Like we had under Mrs Thatcher," shouted someone from the floor, who was obviously mad and should never have been allowed into the hall. Mr O'Donnell held up another board saying "Please don't laugh. The Prime Minister is trying to be serious".

At the end of my historic speech everyone was so impressed that instead of clapping they played the song from the last night of the Proms.

Saturday

After the conference Norman and I have decided to "get away from it all" by going off to the Lake District, to a cottage

belonging to a Mr Wordsworth, who I think is a friend of Norman's.

When we got there it was so old-fashioned that I decided we should stay in a hotel instead. We certainly managed to put all the cares and worries of the conference behind us, as we spent the evening in the Daffodil Lounge with Norman reading out to me bits from the Sunday papers about the conference.

"Look," she said. "Guess who's on the front page? It's Mr Heseltine doing his exercises. And look what's on page 2 — it's Mr Howard with his 279-point plan for stopping crime.

Then she turned to page 3. "Here's a familiar face," she said. "It's Mrs Thatcher denying that she had said you were useless and indecisive." At that point I decided it was time for me to take my traditional walk to see the daffodils with the photographers.

When I came back I found Norman still reading out what Mrs Thatcher said about me in her memoirs, and laughing to herself in a way that I found not inconsiderably annoying. So I decided to fill in the form to hang on our bedroom door, saying what sort of breakfast I wanted. It was a choice between the Full Traditional Lakeland Breakfast, i.e. Cumbrian Sausage, Egg, Bacon and Black Pudding, or the EEC Approved Continental Special, i.e. Low-Cal French Style Croissant with Low Fat Danish Spread and De-Caffeinated Coffee. It was a very difficult decision, so I decided to ask Norman to tick the little boxes for us both.

Monday

When I got back to my desk after our post-conference holiday I was very surprised to find a press release from Mr O'Donnell announcing that he was resigning. I immediately rang him up to ask whether this was true, or was it just another of his special "leaks" like the one saying that the recession is over. He sounded strangely happy and said, "Yes, prime minister, I'm afraid it is true. I have decided to spend more time with my civil service. But do not worry. I have arranged for a very clever man from the Foreign Office to come in to tell you what to do."

"But I already have Mr Hurd to do that," I told him somewhat frostily. It is just as well he is leaving if he is so out of touch with the way things work here.

Tuesday

Today I have made another very important speech about how terrible it is that crime has been rising so much in the last 14 years. I decided to do this after I saw how well Mr Howard's speech had gone down at our Conference. Obviously law and order is the one thing that my government stands for, and it is also very popular. Certainly reducing crime is something that Mrs Thatcher never managed to do during all her years in power. You will not find many mentions of *that* in her new book, which of course I have no intention of reading, especially the bits on pages 78, 84, 102, 154, 186, 212, 236, and 310-84, where she says that I am not up to the job of prime minister.

Wednesday

Mrs Thatcher has been on the television again. Now she says that since my historic speech at the party conference I am a good prime minister. She says there has been a "sea-change" in my attitudes. Obviously this is meant to be a reference to Blackpool, which is by the sea. I pointed this out to my wife Norman, but she said: "The phrase actually comes from *The Tempest*." "I am a busy man," I told her in my stern voice. "I do not have time to sit around reading Wordsworth like you."

Monday

I am in a substantially happy mood due to the no small measure of success achieved by my Charter initiative. Today Mr Waldegrave handed out no less than 738 Charter Badges awarded for excellence in the field of Charter Compliance — no mean feat. Oh yes. Or rather, oh no.

The top award of all goes to the InterCity Customer Services Department for their fine work in keeping customers informed about which trains are late or have been cancelled. Mr Waldegrave summed it up when he told their chief executive: "Well done. Now we get a better price when we sell you off."

Talking of rail privatisation, Mr Macgregor has won a great victory over the so-called rebels. British Rail will now be allowed to bid for the franchises. Except all their bids will be turned down. The rebels seem very happy with this concession and I can now take their names out of my "Rebels" book which I bought last week from Ryman's (who have incidentally been given a charter award for informing customers when they had no more little black books left in stock due to unforeseen demand from Downing Street).

Tuesday

In her book which I have not read, certainly not ten times already, Mrs Thatcher refers to me as "drifting with the tide". This is nonsense as I told a man with a beard on Radio 4's Start The Day. "Oh no," I said, "I did not drift with the tide. I just did what everyone else did." That will finally put paid to Mrs Thatcher.

Wednesday

People are still asking me why there is so much interest in Mrs Thatcher's book. Well, I am not interested. I have not mentioned it at all in my diary. Except for a few times. There is no doubt who is to blame for her being rude about me. It is the media. They have hyped the whole thing out of all proportion. As I told the woman on Radio 4's The World Tomorrow programme: "You are all obsessed by Mrs Thatcher. Let us change the subject and talk about something important. Like what she says about me on page 658 of her book. Which I have not read." I think that draws a line under that!

Thursday

Today is a truly historic day. I met Princess Diana who is the most famous woman in the world. My wife Norman tells me that she has been on the cover of *Hello!* magazine more times than anyone else.

She is not only tall but also in my judgement not inconsiderably attractive. She told me she would like to be a roving ambassador. "You may think," she said, "that all I want to do is fly around the world and be photographed with celebrities and that that would be a waste of time."

"Oh no," I said. "That sounds very important and worthwhile. And it will make you very popular."

"I hope so," she said. "Though it obviously doesn't work for everyone," giving me a very funny look.

Friday

I read in the newspapers that my wife Norman had a private Christmas shopping session in Marks and Spencer. She got the idea from Mrs Bottomley who was frightened to go into the shop

in normal hours in case she was pelted with eggs. Norman told me that she had rung the store saying that her husband was even more unpopular than Mrs Bottomley, and she was afraid of being attacked by old age pensioners shopping for extra thermal underwear.

Norman came home with a very prudent choice of grey pullover, grey socks, grey dressing grown and a rather snazzy pair of grey slippers. "How did you know what to get me?" I asked. "I just pointed to the dummy in the window," she explained, "and told them that I would have all the things that he was wearing."

I am seriously considering awarding a customer care charter badge to Marks and Spencer for their outstanding services to my wife.

Saturday

In our regular weekend emergency Cabinet meeting, Mr Heseltine stood up and did his exercises to show how fit he is. He then announced that all the remaining coal mines are to be closed down.

"I thought we decided to keep them open," I said, quick as a flash, to show Mr Heseltine that I was still prime minister.

"Yes," he said, "but that was six months ago. Everyone's forgotten that now. They are only interested in Mrs Thatcher's book."

Mr Heseltine may have to walk out of *my* Cabinet as well. Oh yes.

Later I brought up the subject of my brilliant new idea: the ID card. "This will stop crime by single-parent mothers claiming social security," I said. "Everyone will have one. Even me."

"That's a good idea," said Mr Waldegrave, as he handed out the tea. "Then at least someone will know who you are."

They all laughed and Mr Clarke (who I'm not sure if he is my friend or not) choked on his cigarette and spilt ash onto his budget figures.

Monday

Today I went to a country called Brussels where I met my old friend Mr Hurd and also a Mr Reynolds who told me that he was the Prime Minister of Ireland, a country which is very near to England on the map. "And what are you doing here?" I said. He replied with something that I did not catch, but I met him later at a big dinner that my friend, Mr Herr Kohl, had laid on. This was very lavish indeed and was held to celebrate Mr Herr Kohl's triumph over the Maastricht Treaty.

But he is not the only one. I have my own personal triumph to record. Although the Germans have told us that Frankfurt is to be the financial capital of the EC, Britain is to get the European Medical Evaluation Agency. This is certainly good news for all medical evaluators everywhere, oh yes. No wonder we were drinking champagne and eating caviare until nine o'clock in the evening!

Meanwhile, Mr Reynolds told me about the trouble in Northern Ireland, which is not in Ireland but in Britain. We decided that something should be done. "But there would have to be peace first," I said, "otherwise how can we stop the war?" Mr Reynolds agreed, so it was a very productive meeting. He could easily become my friend, but Mr Hurd warned me that my other friends, the Ulster Unionists who very kindly vote for me when I am in trouble, would not take kindly to this.

Tuesday

My wife Norman showed me some newspaper pictures of my brother Terry at the circus where he was putting his arm round some pin-up girls, rather like Mr Lamont used to do with Mrs Bottomley. Norman said: "Terry is going to fly round the world having his picture taken with famous people." "He will look very stupid," I told her. "There is nothing more embarrassing than some complete unknown making a fool of himself on the world stage."

"You can say that again," she said. So I did, but it was pointless because I had already said it once. Sometimes women can be very slow off the mark.

November

Monday

Today is a very historic day for the people of Ulster. I am launching a new initiative which will bring an end to the violence and create peace in what Mr Hurd has told me to call "that unhappy land". After all, everyone wants peace, except for the people who don't. And that is why I have begun my initiative by inviting all the people who want peace to come to see me.

The first one to knock at my door this morning was a very large man called Dr Paisley. He is not a doctor at all, but a vicar, which is not inconsiderably confusing.

"As a man of God," I said, "you must be in favour of peace."

"No," he bellowed, and produced a piece of paper which he said was his own solution to all the problems of Northern Ireland. He then read it out in a very loud voice, which made all the biros vibrate on my desk.

"Point One," he began. "No Surrender. Point Two. Now or ever. Point Three. That's it."

He then stormed out, slamming the door so hard that all the biros fell off my desk, and I had to spend 10 minutes picking them up.

I was still on the floor, looking for the one which Chancellor Kohl gave me to celebrate the ratification of the Maastricht Treaty with "Deutschland Über Alles" written on it, when a Mr Molyneaux came in.

"It's alright, prime minister," he said, "there's no need to kneel. We'll support you on rail privatisation as long as you support us over Clause 2."

"What are you talking about?" I asked him. But he had already pulled out several pieces of paper which he said were "The Official Unionist Response To The Search For A Proposal To Bring Peace To Northern Ireland". He began reading this out in a low droning voice, which I am pleased to say did not seem to affect the biros on my desk at all.

"Point One," he began. "We in the Official Unionist Party would like to make it plain that any surrender would be unacceptable to us. Point Two. This surrender would remain unacceptable to us now or at any point in time in the future. Point Three. That is most certainly it, with regard to this one."

I was in no small measure encouraged to hear him. Already I have got two of the main parties agreeing and it cannot be long now before a permanent settlement is reached.

Tuesday

Today my top-level search for peace in Northern Ireland continued, when another man came to see me called Mr Hume. I had taken the precaution of putting all my biros in the top right-hand drawer where I keep my "Bastards" books, in case he should shout at me. But I needn't have bothered. He spoke very quietly and asked if he could read out to me a piece of paper.

"This is the Hume-Adams Plan," he said, "and it will bring complete peace to Northern Ireland in five minutes."

At the mention of the word Adams the door burst open and Mr Hurd came in wearing a balaclava. "Hold it, prime minister," he said. "This plan can only be read out by an actor."

Unfortunately there were no actors in the room, so we had to ask Mr Hume to go away.

Wednesday

Today I had a complete break from my very tiring search for peace in Ulster, when my wife Norman and I were allowed to be the first to see a special new painting of myself by a very famous Irish painter whose name I cannot at the moment recall. The picture showed me standing in front of my library — i.e. *The Complete Encyclopaedia of Useful World Facts*, which I bought from a very persuasive gentleman who came to our door in Huntingdon. Plus all my Wisdens (1957-date, except 1968, which was borrowed by my ex-friend David Mellor and never returned). Plus my complete set of signed Jeffrey Archer novels which he tells me "will one day be a superb investment". Funnily enough these are exactly the same words as those used by the man who sold me my encyclopaedias.

When I asked Norman what she thought of my picture, she said: "Well, John, it is very bland. But that is not the artist's fault."

In the evening Norman and I settled down with our M&S Salmon and Coriander Tikka with some funny bread-like pancakes to watch the programme I have been looking forward to for weeks, the one about how they threw out Mrs Thatcher and chose me instead. "Why doesn't anything on TV have a happy ending any more?" Norman asked, leaving the room.

But I enjoyed it very much indeed, especially the bit where Mrs Thatcher complimented me by saying that I was "a consensus man". This means apparently that everyone agreed that I was the best man for the job, which is quite right. At last Mrs Thatcher has said something which doesn't make her look stupid.

Thursday

Having solved the Irish problem, I today launched an even more historic initiative which I have decided to call "Back to

Basics". This will certainly show people like Mr Lilley and Mr Portfolio who is doing the original thinking around here. At the moment I have only got the title, but I will fill in the rest when I have time.

At our Cabinet meeting I launched the idea, and I told them all — especially Mr Lilley and Mr Portfolio — that whenever they made a speech, they were to be sure to mention the need to "get back to basics".

"But what does that mean?" Mr Waldegrave asked, when he brought in the tea.

"It means exactly what it says," I told him in my sternest Dixon of Dock Green voice. "If we get back to basics then we will be getting back to basics, which is what everyone wants."

They all kept very quiet for some minutes after my charismatic outburst. I noticed that Mr Clarke for some reason kept on writing the number 10 on his notepad (which Sir Robin Butler puts out before our meetings, with a biro next to it).

Mr Gummer eventually asked, on a point of order, why our morning biscuits were now plain and not chocolate-covered as per usual. Mr Waldegrave explained that it was part of a cost-cutting exercise to slash Government spending. He said that he had set up a special new 10-man team to cut down Whitehall waste, and, after a three-month consultation exercise, it had been decided to introduce a cheaper type of biscuit. Tenders had been invited from all the major European biscuit manufacturers and a provisional bid had been accepted from the Danskbik Company of Elsinore, to supply Morning Biscuits. But the decision would be kept under constant review by a 20-man monitoring unit in the Department of Trade and Industry. Who said that my government doesn't get things done?

Friday

I have a new name to put in my "Bastards" book, i.e. Mr Edward Heath, who used to be my friend when he attacked Mrs Thatcher. Now he has attacked me for attacking single parents! What does he know about it? He is not even a single parent. He is no parent at all. Oh no. Sometimes Mrs Thatcher was right about people.

Mr Meyer, my new press officer who took over from Mr O'Donnell, brought in my newspaper this morning (the *Sun*) which tells me what to do. It says that Mrs Thatcher is now going to be in the Cabinet. I wonder if it is true.

Saturday

Sir Richard Body has now been taken out of my "Loonies" book because he has decided not to resign and force a by-election. When I told my wife Norman that he was going to support me, she said: "Then you should put him back in the 'Loonies' book." Politics is sometimes very difficult for a woman to understand, unless she is Mrs Bottomley. Oh yes.

Monday

I am continuing my historic campaign to get Back to Basics. This is entirely my idea which I am working on with Miss Hogg, Mr Waldegrave and my new press adviser Mr Meyer. We have all agreed that we are in favour of the following things:

1. An end to crime.
2. Teaching children the difference between right and wrong.
3. A nationwide campaign to inform the public about the importance of 1 and 2 above.
4. A Back to Basics Charter.
5. A Basics Hotline on which anyone with more suggestions for items can ring up Mr Waldegrave.

This is only a starting point. But to have five points after only a week is a magnificent achievement. Let there be no doubt that it most certainly is. Oh yes.

Tuesday

Everyone is looking forward to the Budget. We used to have it in the spring but my ex-friend Norma Lamont changed it to just before Christmas. When I asked him why, he waved his Thresher's plastic bag and winked at me. "Because everyone drinks a lot at Christmas and so it is the perfect time to put taxes up."

I had to explain this to Mr Clarke who does

Norma's job now, but he did not seem to get the point. "If you ask me," he said, "it is a bloody silly time to have a budget because all it does is create maximum uncertainty at the one time of year when people might spend some money." I'm afraid Mr Clarke is not as brilliant as everyone keeps saying. Also his shoes are never polished which shows an untidy mind.

I asked him what was going to be in his budget and he said it was a secret. "You will just have to wait and see. But I'll tell you one thing — we're running out of things to put VAT on."

It was then that I had one of my not inconsiderably brilliant ideas — the sort of lateral thinking that has put me where I am today! I will hesitate no further and tell you what that idea was. "Well, Mr Clarke," I said, "why don't we put VAT on VAT?" He looked quite astonished, and it was clear that the idea had never even occurred to him.

Wednesday

I was sitting in my office this morning, using the new pencil sharpener I was sent by Eurotunnel. It is in the shape of a tunnel with a French flag at one end and the British flag at the other. You put the pencil in at the French end and nothing happens. I was just about to ask Mr Waldegrave to send it back, when the door flew open and my brother Terry came in, wearing a baseball cap the wrong way round.

"Yo, dude," he shouted, "give me five." I must admit to being in no small measure puzzled. "John," he said, "I've been to the Big Apple. It's really far out, oh yeah." The thought crossed my mind that he must be a big apple short of a picnic, but I did not put him in my Loonies book because he is my brother.

Thursday

Today we all went to Parliament for the Queen's Speech. This is the kind of occasion that shows Britain at its best, like cricket matches, drinking lager in the pub and going off for a curry after evensong. The highlight is when a man called Black Rod bangs on the door with his stick and tells us that the Queen is ready to tell us her ideas for the next Parliament. Then there is a procession, just like at a wedding, with me and Mr Smith at the front like the bride and groom, and Mr Hurd looking like the bride's father.

As usual the Queen was most interesting indeed, and I was particularly pleased that she chose as her main theme the idea of "Back to Basics", although she did not seem to have much idea what it was about. She also said that her government would be abolishing a lot of regulations on businesses. I whispered to Mr Hurd, "Aren't these all the regulations that we brought in?" For some reason he kicked me very hard in the shins.

Friday

When our Cabinet meeting started today everyone was reading the newspapers. Mr Portfolio held up a headline which read "He's Gone At Last — England Supremo Quits After Humiliating Run Of Failure". "It's alright," he explained, with one of his funny twisted smiles, "it's only the football they are talking about."

"I know it is," I said. "I am not a complete idiot."

"Quite right," said Mr Clarke. "You're not a *complete* idiot."

Everyone laughed because Mr Portfolio had rather made a fool of himself. Just then Mr Waldegrave came in with the coffee and an empty tray. "Haven't you forgotten something?" I asked, indicating the absence of our usual biscuits.

"Mrs Bottomley's orders — part of her new drive to abolish fatness."

"Is this true?" I asked the Health Secretary in a stern voice.

"Yes, prime minister," she explained. "Obesity-related diseases are costing the Health Service £25.7 billion a year, which would be much better spent on hiring more managers to make the health service more cost-effective."

Saturday

I was not inconsiderably upset to discover that I am having secret talks with the IRA. Especially when I said I would never have talks with them!

Mr Mayhew, who is a lawyer as well as being in charge of Northern Ireland, had a very clever answer to this.

"You are not talking to Gerry Adams," he said. "You are talking to an actor reading out his words."

"I thought I was talking to you," I replied, but he did not seem to hear me.

Later Mr Meyer came to see me about what I should say if anyone accused me of doing a U-turn.

"You said that your stomach turns at the thought of talks with the IRA."

"Yes," I said, following him closely with my notebook and biro at the ready. "Well, you can still have talks even though your stomach is turning. You see."

He is a very clever man, let there be no doubting this. No wonder I employed him when Mr Hurd told me to give him Mr O'Donnell's job.

Sunday

At last a victory for this country! The England Rugby team have defeated the mighty All Blacks, who are from New Zealand (one of the furthest countries away on my *Daily Telegraph* Wall Map).

I was watching the game on TV yesterday with a one-pack Asda Lo-Cal Shandy when my wife Norman came in and said: "Why are they called the All-Blacks when they are mostly white?"

"It's obvious," I said. "I will tell you later when I have had a word with Mr Hurd."

Women do not understand sport any more than politics.

Monday

Goodness me. I noticed this morning from my Price Waterhouse Advent Calendar that there are by no means a considerable number of days left to Christmas, i.e. not many. Here is my list of items that I would like, which I have put up on the Cabinet notice board for the information of my colleagues. They are:

1. A new set of biros (Ryman's).
2. Notebooks, for listing names under various, i.e. Loonies, Bastards etc. (also from Ryman's).
3. New ring-binder for holding when I am making an idiot of Mr Smith at Question Time (yes, Ryman again!).
4. A book I do not want to be given by anyone! (Clue: it costs £25 and is written by a woman!)
5. Books I would like. My friend Jeffrey Archer's new novel called *Omnibus*. Jeffrey tells me it is his best yet. Also *Howzat! The Tim Rice Book of Cricket Anecdotes* by Tim Rice, and the new book by my favourite author Trollope, which has just come out.
6. A bottle of my favourite after-dinner drink, Bailey's Irish Cream, because I have been spending so much time recently in Dublin! In previous years I have been given this by my ex-friend Norma Lamont, so this year I am hoping someone will be kind enough to step in and fill the gap.

Tuesday

Today is a very historic day, the first ever pre-Christmas Budget. Like everyone else, I was expecting that my new friend Mr Clarke would have to put up taxes quite a lot because we are so much in debt. But, oh no! He did nothing of the sort. There were very loud cheers from our side when he said: "I see no need to put up income tax or VAT." In fact everyone was cheering so loudly that they didn't hear him say, "There's no need because I'm putting up the tax on petrol, cigarettes, insurance, holidays and mortgages instead, not to mention doubling the council tax." What a clever man Mr Clarke is. He has also got another brilliant idea for abolishing unemployment. In future the unemployed will all be called Jobseekers. "We are all Jobseekers, prime minister," he told me, "even those of us who have a job already" — and he gave me a funny smile.

December

Wednesday

Today I flew to Ireland to see my new friend Mr Reynolds. The Irish situation is very complicated, but luckily Mr Hurd was able to come too, so that he could explain the more difficult bits to me while we were having our summit meeting. As soon as the doors were closed, Mr Reynolds began shouting at me, saying that I had told lies about talking to Mr Adams. He continued to scream at me for several hours, until it was time to go in front of the TV cameras to announce our joint communiqué. Mr Reynolds suddenly put on a big smile and said that "we had had a very successful and friendly discussion" although it would be premature to reveal what we had agreed. On the plane home I asked Mr Hurd what we actually had agreed. He said that we had agreed to have another meeting. I was so pleased that we had made such good progress with our Irish peace plan that I celebrated by asking the air hostess for an extra bag of peanuts but I had not found out how to open them before the plane landed.

Thursday

In my judgement, it would be in no way fitting for someone in my position to gloat at the sight of Mrs Thatcher being cross-examined by the Scott Inquiry for eight hours about the so-called "Super-Glue affair". She had only one answer for all the brilliant questions that she was asked, namely: "I was the Prime Minister, and therefore too important to know about what was going on." It was sad to see a

once-powerful figure reduced to making up such flimsy excuses.

Mr Meyer brought in the newspapers and we all read bits of it out to each other in funny voices. Mr Clarke does a very good imitation of Mrs Thatcher and we all had a good laugh, except for Mr Portfolio, who went all po-faced and said it wasn't a laughing matter. Mr Waldegrave then brought in a letter with the tea, and when I opened it, I found it was a message from Mr Justice Scott ordering me to come along to give evidence to his inquiry. What a nerve, I thought. But, quick as a flash, I thought of what I will say to all the clever lawyers — i.e. "I was Foreign Secretary, and therefore too important to know what was going on."

Friday

Let there be no doubt — Mrs Bottomley is a very clever woman. This morning she explained to the Cabinet her latest brilliant plan for saving money on the Health Service. She has decided to close down two more of the hospitals she said she would keep open, including one called Bart's.

"How can you do that?" asked Mr Gummer, rather wetly in my judgement. "It is 800 years old."

"All the more reason why we have to close it," Mrs Bottomley snapped at him. "There is no room for obsolete plant in the market-led health business of the 1990s. Bart's doesn't even have proper office facilities or carparking for the 5,000 new managers who would be required to run it under our reforms."

Everyone was a bit quiet after this, but then Mr Gummer rather unwisely persisted. "Isn't it still going to be rather unpopular?" he asked.

"No, of course not," she said. "I am going to make the announcement about it being closed on Christmas Eve, when everyone will be far too busy celebrating to take any notice."

"In that case," called out Mr Heseltine, who was doing his press-ups in the corner as usual, "I shall announce on Christmas Day that I am the new prime minister."

"You can't do that," Mr Clarke chipped in, "I've already planned to do that myself on Boxing Day."

There is certainly a seasonal mood here in Downing Street! Someone has even added to my list of Christmas presents "No. 7. A new job."

Saturday

I am still working on my "Back to Basics" list. Family life is certainly one of them. Oh yes!

"Then why are you supporting Prince Charles?" asked my wife Norman whilst we were reading *Hello!* magazine at breakfast. "He has not set much of an example with Camilla, has he?"

I was not inconsiderably annoyed by this. "You do not understand at all," I said. "He is the Heir to the Throne. Besides, he may well have been under pressure from a nagging wife. I do not think we are in a position to pass moral judgements."

"That doesn't stop you going on about single mothers, does it?" she said.

When she is in a mood like this there is no point in trying to argue in a rational manner, so I left for the office (downstairs).

Monday

Today was our last day in the House of Commons before the end of term, and the Labour Party tried to catch me out one last time. Mr Smith had done some sums which showed that Mr Clarke's budget was the same as a 7p rise on the income tax. What did I have to say to that? he asked me very rudely in his Scottish voice. I soon sent him packing with a brilliant answer. I jumped up with my ring-binder, which I often think is my equivalent of Churchill's cigar or Mrs Thatcher's handbag, and quick as a flash I replied: "Well, everyone knows that the Labour Party would put up taxes by more than 7p, if they were the government, which they are not — and NO WONDER!"

Everybody laughed and cheered, except the Labour Party and some of our side, who obviously hadn't heard.

Talking of which, my ex-friend Norma Lamont also tried to catch me out by asking me why I had changed my mind about Northern Ireland and was trying to sell out the Protestants. Again I was too quick for him. I pointed out that I hadn't changed my mind, Mr Hurd had changed it for me. This repartee is very easy really when you know how. It is very sad to see Norma becoming so bitter. Why can't he learn to forgive and forget, like I have done with a certain woman whose book I do not want to be given for Christmas!

Tuesday

One of the nice things about being prime minister is that you get hundreds of Christmas cards from very important people all over the world. For instance, in this morning's post I got cards from the following: the Belgian President of the EC, whose name I could not read properly; the manager of Ryman's, thanking me for my custom and including a price list for 1994; Mr Portfolio, who has chosen a picture of himself dressed as a toreador with a sword; Mr Clarke, whose card showed himself photographed outside Number 10 — obviously he had not noticed that it was the wrong door; my brother Terry, whose card shows the Empire State Building and plays "Santa's Coming To Town" when you open it up; and finally one from a Mr Onanugu of Thresher's, asking me to forward it on to Mr Lamont, along with a bill for £19.98p.

One thing that did in no small measure almost spoil my day was the card from Mr Lamont himself. This showed the front door of Rothschild's Bank in the City, and inside was a cutting from the *Telegraph* with a poll which showed that my rating was now even lower than last time. He had written on it: "You are now the most unpopular prime minister since yourself." I shall not be putting this one up, oh no.

Wednesday

Peace on earth, goodwill to men. This year for once it seems the message from the carols is true. And I have played a not inconsiderable role in it. Let there be no doubt about that, thanks to my peace initiative on Ireland. Everyone has been very impressed by my joint-declaration with my new friend, Albert Reynolds, which said that we both wanted peace as soon as possible.

And we are definitely making progress, oh yes. Not so long ago I said I would never talk to the IRA. And now I am. Equally, yesterday I made it clear that there would be no amnesty for terrorists. But today there might be one. So, as you can see, there is plenty of give and take on both sides. Especially mine.

Christmas Day (Chequers)

I got up not inconsiderably early to open my presents. Unfortunately, there seemed to have been a misunderstanding. I had let there be no doubt in my letter to Santa that I particularly did not wish to be given *that* book by *that* woman.

Yet, under the tree there were no less than 17 copies of *The Downing Street Years* all addressed to me. (And all signed by *her*.)

My wife Norman was very sympathetic and told me that the local Oxfam shop would be happy to take them. But when I got down there the lady said they had hundreds already and they could not sell them even for 50p.

So I had to take them home again.

Boxing Day

I am in no small measure angry with the IRA who, in my judgement, are not helping the peace initiative by letting off bombs all over the place.

Mr Hurd rang me up to wish me a Happy Christmas and to ask if I had read his present yet.

I was very short with him and said: "Forget about Christmas. What about the IRA?"

Mr Hurd was, however, very reassuring. "I have made it clear that we will get tough with them if they do not stop the violence."

"But surely", I said in my quizzical Question Time voice, "we have always been tough on the IRA."

"Quite so," said Mr Hurd. "But now we will be *even* tougher."

It is good to have a man as bright as Mr Hurd at one's right hand in times of crisis. Not that this is a crisis. Oh no!

Holiday Boxing Monday

At our regular Cabinet crisis meeting Mr Waldegrave defied Mrs Bottomley's health instructions and brought in some of his wife's mince pies, which were not inconsiderably delicious and I ate an imprudent two of them!

Mr Portfolio asked me, looking even more smug than normal, what exactly our "getting tough" policy entailed.

"Surely it is clear," I explained, putting him in his place. "We get tough by talking to the terrorists and listening to their demands with an open mind."

At this point, Mr Clarke woke up and asked Mr Waldegrave if there were any Alka-Seltzers in his emergency First Aid box.

New Year's Eve (Chequers)

Tonight my wife Norman and I decided to stay up late because it is the New Year. I spent the first part of the evening in my study filling in my New Year's Resolutions in my special New Year's Resolution book (a gift from Mr Cash, the manager of Ryman's). After taking some advice from Miss Hogg, I decided on the following:

1. To be my own man.
2. Never to mention Mrs Thatcher again (see 1993).
3. To get back to basics.
4. Not to repeat myself.
5. To get back to basics.

In no small measure, this is in my judgement a first-class list of resolutions. Oh yes.

When I read it out to Norman, she yawned, obviously because it was very late and time to go to bed. "It is time to drink a toast,"

I said, and poured out two glasses of Norfolk Wassail Non-Alcoholic Punch which Norman had been given on one of her after-hours visits to M and S with Mrs Bottomley. Norman then began to sing "Should old acquaintance be forgot?". "Oh yes," I said, "particularly Mrs Thatcher, Mr Lamont, Mr Mellor and Mr Mates." On this not inconsiderably convivial note, we went to bed, just as the distant village clock struck 9.30.

January 1994

New Year's Day

I got up very early to look at the papers to see who was in my new classless honours list. Top of the list was E.W. Swanton who writes about cricket in the *Daily Telegraph*, and whose autograph I got at the Oval in 1953 when England regained the Ashes. Also I was very pleased that Nat Lofthouse, the famous footballer, has at last been recognised. I used to have his autograph too, but I swapped it for Cyril Washbrook in 1959. This was the first year of my new "classless honours" when ordinary members of the public could write in to Mr Waldegrave to suggest their own names for honours. It was interesting how many people had written in from a place called Grantchester suggesting that Lord Archer should be made honorary prime minister. I don't think some people have quite got the idea of my new "Honours Charter" yet. However I was glad to see that a lot of people I know had got in, e.g. Mr O'Donnell, who is to become Sir Gus, and the man who runs the THF Windermere-Crest Hotel in the Lake District where I go to recharge my batteries after Party conferences. When Norman read through the names, she said, "This lot haven't got much class." "That is the whole point," I told her, in a frosty voice.

Sunday

I have had to stay in all today because I have been expecting a telephone call from Mr Adams, the leader of the Sinn Fein, to say that he has accepted my great Ulster peace initiative. Obviously the IRA are taking my tough stand very seriously, as they have been letting off bombs all over the place. But they have not yet had the courage to ring me up directly, and I have decided that if they have not responded within a week, I will have to warn them that they will only have another two weeks before I issue another ultimatum giving them not more than a month to agree to have talks with me.

Monday

The papers are once again trying to make trouble. Instead of concentrating on my great peace initiative and my very popular classless honours list, they have somehow managed to dig up a totally irrelevant story about one of my very junior ministers called Mr Yeo. All he has done is to have a child with some lady who is not his wife. "To my mind this is entirely his own affair," I told Norman, as I put the remaining portion of Safeway Christmas pudding into the microwave. "It *is* an affair," said Norman crossly. "I thought you were meant to be in favour of the family." "I am," I said, "and so is Mr Yeo. And now he's got two of them."

Anyway, I have issued a statement saying that "I give Mr Yeo my full support." "Just like you did to Mr Mellor," said Norman.

The family is all very well but after an extended Christmas holiday it is quite a relief to go back to work downstairs.

Tuesday

The tabloid press are still going on about Mr Yeo. I am not going to be told who I should have in my government by the *Sun*, oh no.

Wednesday

The *Sun* says that Mr Yeo should resign. I agree. It is time for him to go. I cannot have ministers making my "family values" campaign look ridiculous. Not that my "family values" campaign is about families. As Mrs Bottomley so brilliantly explained on Newsnight, the Today programme, GMTV, the Big Breakfast and many other shows, the "back to basics" campaign is really about teaching children to read and write. She was particularly forceful today, sweeping aside all the irrelevant questions put to her by the interviewers, and talking very slowly and loudly. She rather reminded me of someone, but I could not quite remember who.

Thursday

The Yeo affair is over. I have drawn a line under it.

Unfortunately no one has told the newspapers. Now they say that Mr Yeo has had another love child. But this one was a long time ago. And I have drawn a line under this one, too.

I asked the Cabinet whether any of them wished to spend more time with their families, as it would help me greatly if I could know in advance. I am now filling in my new Year-At-A-Glance planner, and it is not inconsiderably annoying to have to keep putting in new Government vacancies to fill — three this week!

However, the Cabinet were all very quiet indeed, which shows they have nothing to hide.

Sunday

Today I was invited onto Sir David Frost's television show! Who says I am unpopular? He is a very tough interviewer in my judgement and asked me whether I had had a nice Christmas.

I told him that my Back to Basics campaign had nothing to do with people's private lives. It was about getting back to basics.

Mr Frost was very impressed by this reply and nodded politely. A line has definitely been drawn under this now.

Monday

I was not inconsiderably annoyed this morning to see the tabloid press — i.e. the *Daily Telegraph* — had "raked up" six more Conservative MPs who have got love children.

There was at least one good piece of news — i.e. a Mr Ashby MP who has been setting a first-class example of saving money by sharing bedrooms when he is on holiday abroad with his male friends. I am sure now we have heard the last of all this.

Tuesday

The newspapers do not seem to have got the message about the line I have drawn under the sleaze... Not that there is any sleaze, it is all just allegations — like this morning when the papers said that Mrs Lady Porter had sold lots of council houses to Tory MPs in order to buy their votes. But

fortunately all this happened in the days of Lady Thatcher, which means that it is all her fault and not mine — just like the so-called Iraqi Super-Glue Affair which I have got Mr Scott to look into. When will the newspapers get the point that everything that has gone wrong with this country is the fault of Mrs Thatcher? "Including making you prime minister," my wife Norman added, totally missing the point as she often does when it comes to politics.

Wednesday

Today Mr Scott has asked me to give evidence to his enquiry. What cheek! Surely it is obvious that if I knew anything about what had happened, I wouldn't have asked him to find out for me. However he soon realised his mistake, when he and a lady called Mrs Baxendale started asking me questions, and I was able to reply: "I did not know what was going on, and even if I did, I can't remember." Everyone's mouths fell open with amazement at my brilliant replies, and soon Mr Scott said I could go home, as I "obviously didn't have a clue" what I was doing. He is a very shrewd man, and I was obviously right to give him the job.

Thursday

Tonight we had a special dinner to say goodbye to Mr O'Donnell, and to thank him for all he has done to put across my policies to the press and to win their support. Naturally some of the papers were not asked to the dinner because of their traditional hostility to the Conservative Party — i.e. the *Sun*, the *Daily Mail* and the *Daily Telegraph*. We had a very nice dinner and I am glad to say that I made a very witty speech, which consisted of reading bits out of this diary. Everyone laughed, which was odd, since the extracts were very serious.

Friday

Mr Smith has in no small measure annoyed me. Today in the House of Commons he asked me why I had put up taxes more than anyone else in history. Luckily I had a brilliant impromptu reply typed out by Miss Hogg. "If the Labour Party were in power, which they are not, they would put up taxes by much more." This silenced Mr Smith, who immediately went on to ask the question again. I repeated my answer and everyone groaned, obviously because Mr Smith had not got my point. I then found in my ring-binder another note typed by Miss Hogg, saying: "If you are desperate, accuse the Labour Party of making up smears against you and read out this list:

"1. Labour said Tories Sell Honours. Not true.

"2. The *Guardian*, i.e. a Labour Party paper, said that the

Saudis had given money to Michael Heseltine. Not true.

"3. Labour said we were closing down hospitals. Not true, as Mrs Bottomley has made clear on many occasions.

"4. Labour said I was no good. Not true.

"P.S. If you are really in trouble, remind them about all the great Labour disasters — e.g. the lavender list 1976, the groundnuts scheme 1949, the Zinoviev letter 1924 and Mr Dalton's budget leak 1946."

When I read this out there were jeers and shouts of "pathetic", "utterly dismal" and "grotesque" — which shows how unpopular the Labour Party is.

Monday

Mr Howard, although he is in my "Bastards" book, has got some very good ideas about making the police more efficient. In future, local Conservatives will be in charge of all police authorities to make sure there is no bias.

And moreover the courts will now be assessed on a performance-related basis, i.e. the more people who are sent to prison, the more money the judges will be paid. These are in no small measure excellent proposals and no one could possibly object to them.

Tuesday

Mr Howard's plans are in ruins. They have been attacked by everyone, including Lord Whitelaw and the Lord Chief Justice. I was always suspicious of them and intended to tell Mr Howard so at the time. It just goes to show that once you have been put in my "Bastards" book you are likely to remain there. Oh yes.

Wednesday

Someone has been claiming to have thought up my Back to Basics idea. "It is a silly old woman who writes books," I told my wife Norman. "I thought you weren't going to mention Mrs Thatcher again," she said as she defrosted the freezer and took out all the individual portions of M&S Vegetarian Steak 'n' Kidney Pie and piled them on the table.

"Not her," I said in a cross voice. "But somebody called Dame Barbara Cartland."

Norman looked surprised. "She writes rubbish," she said, "so perhaps she did think it up."

"I hope you can refreeze those pies without risk of food poisoning," I said, skilfully changing the subject. Then she told me to be quiet because she wanted to watch the end of a new soap called *Middlemarch*.

February

Monday

I'm afraid it was not a very good start to the week. All the papers had a picture of me with my head in my hands looking very miserable, as if something might be wrong with the country. In fact I was not miserable at all. I was just feeling rather tired and depressed. But then everything changed. The door burst open and in came Mr Meyer (who has taken over from Sir Gus O'Donnell). Jumping onto my desk, and incidentally knocking over all my biros, he pointed at the pictures and shouted: "That's the last time those Bastards will be able to try anything like that. From now on it's no more Mr Nice Guy. We're going to kick some ass."

"Oh yes," I replied. "That is exactly what I was going to say, as soon as I heard you say it. I'm going to show them all who is the boss around here. What do I do first?" Mr Meyer then pulled out a list of people I had to be very rude to. He called it "The Getting Tough List".

1. Mr Smith.
2. Sir George Gardiner (memo: I must find out who he is).
3. The press.
4. The media.
5. The left.
6. The right.
7. Everyone else.

I cannot wait to begin and, to show Mr Meyer I meant business, I threw away all the biros that didn't work properly, especially the one saying "Portfolio For PM" which he gave me for Christmas as a joke.

Wednesday

Today I found out who Sir George Gardiner is. He is the chairman of the 1992 Committee, which is not to be confused with the 1922 Committee. Not that I would confuse them, because I know the difference. One is 70 years older than the other, as you can tell by the dates! I was meant to have a meeting with Sir George today at 5.30, so that he could tell me that I should resign. But

before he could sit down, Mr Meyer came bounding in the door and said: "The Prime Minister is very busy and hasn't got time to talk to right-wing loonies like you." Mr Gardiner then looked a bit puzzled and went out saying that he would come back at a more convenient time. Mr Meyer immediately began calling up lots of journalists and told them (off the record) that I had got "really bloody tough with that Bastard Gardiner".

Thursday

The papers have got something right about me at last. They all had the same headline "Major Gets Tough With Tory Right", and described how I had kicked Mr Gardiner out of my office after only two minutes.

In the afternoon I decided to get tough with Mr Smith. He asked me in the House of Commons why I had let the Germans buy up Rover Cars. I jumped to my feet and replied: "Your question shows that you don't know anything about the free market. We *do* which is why we paid British Aerospace a huge sum to buy Rover in the first place." Everyone on the Labour side laughed at this brilliant reply. But I had not finished with Mr Smith. I am merciless these days! "I see that you have obviously prepared all your questions in advance," I told him, reading out what Sir Robin Butler had prepared for me to say. Mr Smith looked so shocked that he had to sit down.

Friday

Today it is Mr Clinton's turn to feel the lash of my toughness. Although he knew perfectly well that it would considerably annoy me, he allowed Gerry Adams to go to America and be on all the television programmes saying that he wanted peace and that I was against it. So no one knew that I am actually for peace. Which I am. Very much so. As Mr Adams well knows because I told him, during the talks that we didn't have last year. But once again Mr Meyer has come to the rescue. This morning there were huge headlines in all the papers saying "Major Blasts Clinton", "Major Lashes Adams", "Anglo-US Rift Worst Since Boston Tea Party". Who says I am not achieving anything? Although I am afraid Mr Hurd was quite upset when he saw how tough I was getting. "You should try it too, Douglas," I said. "Perhaps you could start by pulling the troops out of Bosnia. That would show everyone that we mean business."

Saturday

Mr Clinton does not seem to be getting my toughness message. He has let into America yet another undesirable self-publicist —

i.e. the woman I never mention (Mrs Thatcher). How dare she go on television and say I am doing nothing about Bosnia. That is my job. And let there be no doubt about it in her mind.

Sunday

I am in no small measure surprised to see that I have given an interview to the *Sunday Times*. Apparently I have told the whole Conservative Party to stop saying I am useless behind my back. And they have got the message. Because today a man from the 1922 Committee came up to me and said "You're useless" to my face.

It also says in the papers that Mr Smith is suddenly very popular. Yet he is not tough at all. Oh no. Perhaps I am being too tough. I suggested this to Mr Meyer, who told me to shut up, mind my own business and leave these things to people who knew what they were doing. I agreed entirely.

Monday

I am not inconsiderably annoyed with yet another of my MPs. This one has died, thereby causing a by-election. As I told Sir Norma Fowler, this is something that we do not want until the public realises how well my Back to Basics policy is working. Sir Norma looked at me in a peculiar fashion and said: "Ahem, I wouldn't worry about the by-election, prime minister. I think the result of that is a foregone conclusion."

"That is very reassuring," I told him.

"No, I don't think you understand, prime minister. This particular MP was found in rather peculiar circumstances. He was wearing women's clothes and eating an orange."

"Oh dear," I said, "that does sound rather worrying."

"He also had a plastic bag over his head," Sir Norma went on.

"Oh good," I told him, "that means no one will know who he was."

Tuesday

The newspapers have completely missed the point yet again. They say that the dead MP means the end of my "Back to Basics" policy. Why should it be? They could not be more wrong. I never said that Back to Basics was to do with eating oranges and putting bags over your head. If you go through my famous Conference speech last year, you will not find a single reference to men wearing women's underwear or eating any sort of fruit. Oh no. I was very pleased when Mr Meyer told me that I had already made a press statement to this effect, saying that Back to Basics was about:

1. Widening the M25 to 14 lanes.

2. Increasing the fines for users of the deadly cannabis drug to £25,000 (this is a brilliant idea of Mr Howard's).

3. VAT on everything.

Wednesday

Yet another of my ministers seems to have resigned. Apparently the reason is that he didn't have an affair with his researcher. When I told this to my wife Norman, she said: "Well in that case you should resign, too, for not having an affair with that cook."

"You have missed the point," I replied, giving her one of my stern looks. "I didn't write any silly poetry, unlike Mr Hartley Booth. Listen to this one...

"Labour is red, Tories are blue,
I'm an MP
Your place or mine?"

Thursday

I have finally lost my patience with all the papers. How can they possibly link Mr Booth's personal tragedy over his researcher with my Back to Basics campaign? Look back at my Conference speech and you will not find even the tiniest reference to the writing of love poems or the cuddling of research assistants in bed at night. I was very pleased when Mr Meyer showed me an article I had written for this morning's *Daily Express*, which made exactly this point — i.e. that Back to Basics is about:

1. Privatising the railways.

2. Closing down Guy's Hospital (this is a brilliant idea of Bottomley's).

3. Building a much-needed dam in Malaysia to help the Third World.

Mr Meyer also told me that I was flying out to Russia this evening to be photographed with Mr Yeltsin.

"Why?" I asked him.

"To show people", he explained, "that there is more to Majorism than just men writing poems and putting bags over their heads."

Friday

It is very cold in Russia, and Mr Meyer has given me a special fur hat to wear. When I asked him: "Is it to keep my head warm?" he said: "No, it is so that people will take photographs of you and compare you to real statesmen like Mr Macmillan."

Poor Mr Yeltsin has a very bad cold and at our meeting he kept swigging cough mixture from a bottle marked 90° proof. But we soon got down to serious negotiation about how to bolster up Mr Yeltsin's popularity. "What I really need", he told me, "is to be visited by a really important and respected world-figure from your country, like your prime minister Mrs Thatcher. Or if she is busy, your Queen."

Saturday

Today I flew back after my historic diplomatic triumph in agreeing to allow the Queen to visit Russia. When I got home there was a message on my answerphone from my brother Terry, who is writing a book about our family history, and wants to know if I have done anything interesting that ought to be in it.

I was just thinking what would be suitable for him to include when Mr Waldegrave came in looking very pleased and told me that he had just personally taken a call on our new Charterline. This is the 37th call in only six months, and Mr Waldegrave has worked out that each call only costs the taxpayer £11,426, which is surely a bargain in anyone's book!

This call was from a lady in Heckmondwyke who put her money in a stamp machine but nothing came out because the machine was empty. Mr Waldegrave was able to tell her that since Post Office Counter Services was now a quango, it was not the Government's business and so he could not help her. Nevertheless he would arrange for her to be sent a new Charter booklet called *You and Your Post Office*, plus details of how she could get counselling for customers involved in Post-Post Office Traumatic Stress Situations. I must remember to tell my brother to have a whole chapter in his book on how I started the Citizen's

Charter. Who says I have no ideas? First the Charterline, then Back to Basics. Whatever will I think of next?

Sunday

There is a strange message on my answerphone from Mrs Thatcher, telling my wife Norman that she must not wear State jewels that do not belong to her. I told the machine firmly that my wife can wear whatever she likes. That certainly shut her up. All she could do was say the same thing over and over again, just like she did when she was Prime Minister. Then she let out a high-pitched whine. How pathetic! I must tell Norma not to wear the jewels ever again.

Mr Clarke has been on Desert Island Discs, which I have been on first, and I have to say his choice of records was in my judgement very poor indeed. He had one record by a Monk called Thelonius and another one by Little Richardjohn who is a journalist on the *Sun*. It shows that he is completely out of touch. Yet he says that he wants to be Prime Minister! I told Norman as we listened to it that Mr Clarke came over as an absurd figure.

"Unlike this?" she asked, holding up a picture of me in a hat in Russia. Her loyalty is in no small measure gratifying.

Monday

Mr Hurd came to see me with some good news from Bosnia. He says that we do *not* have to bomb the Serbs after all, which we did not want to do anyway but which Mr Clinton told us we had to. Apparently, Mr Hurd says, all the Serbian guns have been moved away from the hills around Sarajevo.

"Where are they now?" I asked him.

"They've gone to bomb Muslims in Tuzla and Bihac," he told me.

"That'll show them we mean business," I told him in my Getting Tough voice.

March

Monday

You'll never guess where I am writing my diary from this week! I am 37,000 feet above the ground in a very big aeroplane, with my new friend Mr Clinton. He has allowed me to fly in his plane and also to be photographed with him, to make up for having permitted Gerry Adams to come to America. Now it is my turn to be on television all the time. For example, today I have been on the following programmes already:

Hi There Ohio
Dallas Drivetime
The Reverend Hiram Greenback's All-Nite Prayerathon

They were all on in the middle of the night, which is when most Americans watch television, according to my new press adviser Mr Meyer. Talking of which, Mr Meyer is a considerably better press adviser than Mr O'Donnell ever was, in my judgement. For instance, he has already discovered that my grandfather was an American, which I did not know. Apparently he was called Abraham Ball-Lincoln.

Tuesday

Today Mr Meyer has arranged for me to go to Pittsburgh, to be photographed looking for my grandfather in the public library. We started with the telephone directory, but there was no one called Ball-Lincoln there. There was however a man called Major Major III living at 4006 Al Capone Drive. I was photographed outside his house, but he came out very angrily asking who I was and threatening to shoot me if I didn't leave immediately. I made a note to tell my brother Terry about this, because it will make an interesting anecdote for his book about our family.

Wednesday

Today I was photographed having breakfast with Mr Clinton at the White House. We had some very nice waffles with maple syrup, and Eggs Over Easy which are like our fried eggs except they have been turned over. Just imagine, my grandfather must have eaten these every morning in his home at Pittsburgh, when he lived there, if he did. Anyway, this was all to show that Mr Clinton and I still have a special relationship, just like the woman I don't mention did with President Reagan. Except that ours is more special, because Mrs Thatcher was never invited to stay at the White House. When Mr Clinton and I were alone, he slapped me on the shoulder and said: "Sure we have a special relationship, John. I think you are a very special

asshole." He certainly has a great sense of humour!

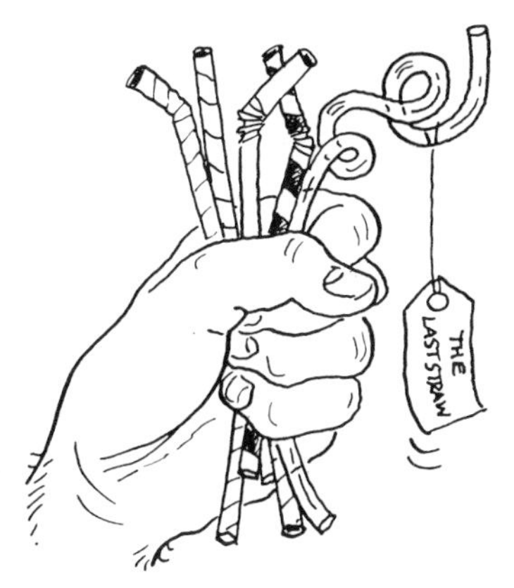

Thursday

Today I returned home, to find that, as usual when I go away, the whole country has fallen apart. Things are so bad that they are even saying that Mr Heseltine should be prime minister. This is a very silly idea. Don't they remember that he tried to be prime minister before, and I won? Apparently, Mr Heseltine had done very well at the Scott inquiry, by blaming everyone except himself. What's so clever about that? I did exactly the same thing when I went to the Scott Inquiry, and no one said I should be prime minister.

Friday

When I came into this morning's Cabinet meeting Mr Heseltine was by mistake sitting in my chair. He laughed good-naturedly when I pointed this out, as did the rest of the Cabinet, and went back to his usual place. I then announced my new plan about the Scott inquiry, which had been thought up for me by Sir Robin Butler. Sir Robin came in with a number of straws in his hand, and walked over to Sir Nicholas Lyell, who I confess I had never heard of before. Sir Robin said, "Choose a straw, Sir Nicholas. Whoever gets the short one has to take all the blame for Matrix Churchill." Sir Nicholas picked one out and Sir Robin immediately said: "Oh dear, it's you. Well, that's that then. You had better start clearing your desk." I could see that Sir Nicholas was very upset, as he kept asking how long all the other straws were. But Sir Robin told him: "The length of the straws is a matter of national security and it is not in the public interest for you to know." We have now drawn a line under this whole business, and let us hope that this is an end to the whole unnecessary Scott inquiry which I set up.

Saturday

I refuse to be annoyed by all the papers saying that Mr Heseltine is now prime minister. For a start, Mr Heseltine has told me personally that I have his 100% support until he becomes prime minister. Surely nothing could be plainer than that? I explained this to my wife Norman at breakfast, where she had made some special "waffles sunny side up", which Mrs Clinton had shown her how to do.

I told her that Mr Heseltine could not do my job because he wasn't fit. "That hasn't stopped you," she replied, giving me a funny look and popping a fried egg into my coffee.

Sunday

Mr Clinton may not be my friend after all. My press adviser Mr Meyer came round urgently to tell me that Mr Clinton is involved in the Whitewater scandal (which I think is something they drink at breakfast). Anyway, Mr Meyer said to me confidentially: "The mounting evidence of sleaze and corruption makes it very risky to be associated with such a tarnished figure." "That is why President Clinton won't talk to you anymore," added my wife missing the point again.

Monday

I was very pleased to see Lord Hailsham on Panorama being interviewed about the Matrix-Churchill business. At last someone has talked some sense about this very minor and unimportant crisis which could bring down my government. Lord Hailsham said that the whole thing should be left to the lawyers to sort out, except for Lord Justice Scott, who, as he said, obviously knows nothing about the law, since he keeps on having to ask everyone what the truth is. Lord Hailsham also pointed out, quite correctly in my judgement, that Mr Heseltine is not a lawyer, and therefore does not know what he's talking about. Mr Heseltine said that there had been a cover-up, and that he was the only minister who was innocent. What rubbish. Michael knows perfectly well that we were all in the cover-up together, although of course there wasn't one.

Tuesday

Mr Waldegrave has not inconsiderably blotted his copy book. He has made a speech saying that all politicians have to tell lies. To prove his point he said Mr Callaghan used to lie and Mr Callaghan said that that wasn't true. Which made Mr Waldegrave look like a liar. Which he had said he was already. It was all not inconsiderably confusing.

Wednesday

The newspapers keep on saying that my great Irish peace initiative has failed, just because the IRA keeps on firing mortars at Heathrow Airport. That has nothing to do with the initiative,

which is still just as much on the table as it ever was. It is now up to us to move forward, in the spirit of the declaration. If the men of violence do not want to be involved in the peace process, then we shall just have to achieve peace without them.

Thursday

My ex-friend Norma Lamont has made a bit of a fool of himself, I am sorry to say! He has been objecting to a very funny advertisement which my wife Norman and I have been watching every night on the television. We have even made a tape of it! It shows Mr Healey, who used to be Labour Chancellor (in the days when there used to be such things!), standing outside a Thresher's wine shop making a funny face. Norma is very upset that they did not hire him to do the advertisement, as he is an ex-chancellor and he needs the money. Mr Lamont cannot see that it is only meant to be a joke, and as I told my wife Norman, in politics you sometimes have to learn to put up with a joke. "Yes," my wife said, "the British public has put up with you for three years. They obviously have a great sense of humour." I did not find her remark in any measure amusing, I have to say.

Friday

At our Cabinet meeting this morning Mr Waldegrave had some more good news about the success of my great Citizen's Charter initiative. Apparently we have now spent £5 billion on the new Charterline, which is much more than Mrs Thatcher ever did.

The statistics are as follows:

Calls regarding cones on motorways	874,000
Number of cones removed	2
Number of calls on other subjects	1
Cost per call	£710

"This shows", Mr Waldegrave said, "that the prime minister's Charter idea has been a great triumph."

"Is that another of your lies?" asked Mr Clarke, and many of the Cabinet began to laugh, which in my judgement was very unfair. "Cones are no laughing matter," I told them in my stern voice. "Perhaps," Mr Heseltine suggested, "we should be called the Cone-servative Party." I am beginning to see Mr Lamont's point. Some jokes are not funny at all, even if you have a sense of humour, which I certainly do, oh yes.

Saturday

My wife Norman and I were woken up very early this morning by a figure kneeling at the foot of our bed. He was dressed in a long black cloak and wore a funny hat with a bobble on it, like you see in the advertisements for Renault cars. "Forgive me, prime minister," he said, "for I have sinned." I then realised that it was Mr Gummer. Speaking in a low voice he said, "I want to make a confession. For many years I have supported our party's plans to build more and more roads and to run down public transport. But my eyes have now been opened and I have seen the light. I recognise that the motor car is a veritable instrument of Satan, like unto the women priests." I asked him to get up off his knees and to go home and lie down, as he was obviously not feeling very well.

Monday

I am in Sarajevo for what my press adviser Mr Meyer said would be a morale-boosting trip.

"Yes," I said. "It will cheer up the Yugoslavians to have a world leader such as myself coming to visit them."

"I hadn't thought of that," said Mr Meyer. "But it has certainly cheered up the people back home to have you out of the country."

Tuesday

I have now returned to England and it is good to be eating a proper English breakfast. In Yugoslavia no one had heard of Coco-Pops, let alone Pop-Tarts! Things are in no small measure extremely serious there, oh yes!

Mr Meyer tells me my mission was a great success. Apparently I did not say anything and had my photograph taken everywhere I went. This is apparently the mark of a true statesman. Unlike Mr Smith, for example, who never goes anywhere and has always got interesting things to say. The papers claim that he is going to be the next Prime Minister. "Rubbish," said my wife Norman loyally. "Michael Heseltine is."

Wednesday

I am extremely sorry to see that the woman whose name I don't mention has collapsed from exhaustion in Chile which is in

South America. This shows how silly it is to try and go on and on when everyone knows that you are past it.

"That is very true," said my wife Norman, giving me one of her funny looks. "I am glad you see it that way."

Mrs Thatcher is in for another shock when she discovers that she is not the only one who can stand up for Britain against Europe.

I have made a speech today in Plymouth (which is not in South America) which makes it clear in no uncertain terms that I am not going to be pushed around by Monsieur Delors and all his friends. Oh yes, or rather oh oui!

Thursday

Today I have got even tougher than I got yesterday. When Mr Smith tried to make trouble about Europe in the House of Commons I was ready for him. I jumped to my feet with my ring-binder and read out one of my spontaneous jokes. "The right honourable gentleman is a poodle," I said, "doing a wee-wee on the lamp post of Brussels." Everyone laughed, even Mr Smith who pretended to look pleased. Mr Hurd was so amused he put his head in his hands and kept saying "Oh no!" again and again.

Friday

I have had an idea which will in my judgement put an end to all the silly criticism in the press. I have decided to bring in Sir Bernard Ingham who was Mrs Thatcher's press adviser and who made her very popular in the opinion polls. Sir Bernard is a bluff Yorkshireman who speaks his mind, which everyone says is a good thing.

He came into my office and said: " 'Appen this'll be hard work. You're totally bloody useless." We have made a very good start.

Monday

In our regular emergency Cabinet meeting Mr Heseltine considerably annoyed me by smiling and whistling all the time. "Things are very serious, Michael," I said in my stern voice. "I know," he said and burst out laughing.

Mr Portfolio, who is not my friend, asked me to clarify my position on European Enlargement. "It is very complex," I said, "but Mr Hurd will explain." Mr Hurd then unfolded a chart with all the countries and their flags on it. Under every country was a number of votes, just like with Torvill and Dean. I interrupted Mr Hurd to point out this ice-skating parallel and Mr Redwood said: "Oh I see. Britain is going to lose again."

Anyway, according to Mr Hurd, the whole question is how

many points you need to stop the Europeans doing whatever they want. We say 23. And they say 27. "There is no room for compromise," I told everyone. "We stand firm at 23."

Tuesday

Mr Hurd has come back from Greece having agreed to 27. He tells me this is a great triumph. "Did we not stand firm on 23?" I asked him crossly. "We did," he replied, "but then we gave in. It was a tactical move. However the decision is up to you, prime minister. I can only advise you that if you don't agree to 27 then I'll resign and bring down your government."

"That sounds sensible," I replied. "But I would like some time to think about it."

"You've got thirty seconds," he said. "The EC deadline is at 5 o'clock."

"Well then," I concluded. "It is agreed."

Wednesday

Mr Ingham has not proved as successful as I hoped. All the papers are saying that I did a humiliating U-turn over the Eurovoting affair. It is however quite obvious that this is untrue. Mr Hurd did it.

Thursday

The papers now say that I should resign and Mr Heseltine should take over as prime minister. Don't they remember what happened last time they said this? Mr Heseltine looked foolish and I became prime minister. The same thing will happen this time, particularly as I am already prime minister.

April

Friday April 1st

Today the Cabinet played a very funny joke on me. They all said that I should resign immediately. How I laughed! It was an April Fool, of course, and they were just teasing me. Strangely, it was after 12 o'clock when you are not supposed to do April Fool tricks any more, but I said nothing about this. I did however assure them that I had no intention of resigning. Then they all laughed and told me that this was the best joke of all.

Saturday

Mr Clarke had a rather late April Fool joke, which was telling everyone that his tax increases were only the equivalent of two pints of beer a week.

We all believed this until Mr Portfolio spoilt the fun by pointing out that actually the new taxes will cost every taxpayer the equivalent of five bottles of whisky a day.

Tuesday

Today I went to Essex which is a place near London which is famous for its jokes and where everyone is a Conservative. Mr Meyer said that it was another morale-boosting exercise. I said: "What is the point of that if they are all Conservatives anyway?" "It is *your* morale that will be boosted, not theirs," he told me.

When we got to Billericay it was raining and there was no one there. "For security reasons, they do not know that you are coming," explained Mr Meyer with an odd look on his face.

On our way home, Mr Meyer asked me if I had heard the latest Essex joke. "You," he said. I did not get it.

Monday

Today is yet another historic day. After the success of my "meet the people" tour of Basildon and Solihull, I have decided that I will personally take charge of our campaign to win the local elections. When I summoned Sir Norma Fowler to tell him this, he went white with pleasure. "But surely, prime minister, you will be too busy running the country to worry about that?"

"Oh no," I replied, "it is my duty to be answerable to the voters at all times. That is why this very afternoon I have agreed to do a phone-in programme at Radio Trent, which is a place near Birmingham." At this point Sir Norma was so delighted that he fell to the floor and would not wake up for several minutes.

Tuesday

My visit to Radio Trent has been a great success! During the hour I was on several people rang me up. Unfortunately the lines to Radio Trent must have been very bad, because they all had to shout at the top of their voices. One poor woman obviously got a crossed line because she kept yelling: "You are totally useless. You have made a mess of everything. You are a total idiot. We should never have got you in." As I told the man who put on the records, the lady was obviously complaining about some workmen and she should contact the appropriate Charter-line and talk to Mr Waldegrave. Clearly I had persuaded all the listeners that it would be good to vote Conservative, because after this no one else rang up and the man had to play "The Shrimp Boats Are A-Comin' In" by Miss Alma Cogan twelve times to fill up the rest of the programme.

Wednesday

I have decided to take personal charge of something else — the great commemoration of our historic victory on D-Day 50 years ago. Like my predecessor Sir Winston Churchill I have turned my office into a "war room" with my *Daily Telegraph* Wall Map on the floor and the biros all over it showing the hotels where the various heads of state are going to stay for the celebrations.

For example the grey biro represents myself, the red, white and blue one stands for Mr Clinton and the one with the words "Non A L'Agneau Anglais" on it is President Mitterrand. For the public to see me organising a famous victory like World War Two should do wonders for my ratings in the polls. Already people are beginning to see me as Churchill, and wherever I go they give me his famous V-sign, except that it is the wrong way round.

Thursday

I was able to announce to the Cabinet this morning the good news that we have won the Test Match. This is a very good omen for the Euro-Elections, and I suggested that a national day of celebration should be held, with myself taking personal charge.

The Cabinet obviously agreed, as no one said anything for

some time, and Mr Howard then broke the silence by reading out his latest list of U-turns. These were:

1. His pledge that murderers of policemen should be jailed for life. He has now found that this is not practicable.

2. His pledge not to censor nasty videos for the under-5s. He has now found that it would be more popular to do the opposite.

3. His pledge to stop mini-cabs doing U-turns in the street. He has now discovered that he is in favour of U-turns, although he may change his mind tomorrow.

Friday

When I woke up this morning there was a message on my answering machine from Mr Clinton's secretary. It said: "Hi there, the President would like you to know that he has kicked ass Serb-wise. He thanks you for your support in the historic bombing decision, and hopes you have a nice day."

I immediately rang Mr Hurd to tell him what the President had said and I had decided. Mr Hurd was obviously jealous of my place on the world stage, and said in his toffee-nosed way: "I don't think you'd better claim any credit for this one. It could lead to another world war. I'd blame it on General Rose and the UN if I were you." Mr Hurd has missed the point, I am afraid. I have decided to invite General Rose, Dame Vera Lynn and Mr Atherton to join my war Cabinet in planning the D-Day Invasion.

Monday

Mr Tim Bell who is helping me with ideas for D-Day has told me that we are not going to mention the Germans in our celebrations as this would be tactless and they might not buy any more of our companies.

"We were fighting the Nazis, not the Germans," he explained.

Afterwards I looked on my map for Naziland but I could not find it. Perhaps he meant Swaziland, which I did find, only it was in Africa.

Tuesday

Let it be known that I was not inconsiderably annoyed with Mrs Beckett who is pretending to be

Mr Smith because he has hurt his leg. She accused me of trying to use the D-Day celebrations as propaganda to win votes in the Euro-elections. This is typical of the Labour Party and I will say so in my big D-Day speech asking people to vote Tory.

Wednesday

I had a request today from my friend Mrs Bottomley asking to be moved to another job. Obviously, now that she has closed down all the hospitals there is nothing left for her to do.

"Perhaps you should have my job," I joked off-the-cuff.

"Thank you," she said, as she tried to sit in my seat, but unfortunately for her Mr Heseltine would not move from it.

Later on in the House of Commons Mrs Boothroyd, the Speaker, in no small measure irritated me by telling me to apologise to Mrs Beckett for calling her a liar.

"How dare a woman tell me what to do," I said to my wife Norman as I was watching the Test Match Highlights on Sky. "Turn that off," she said to me. "It's time for The Bill." And so it was.

May

Monday

The newspapers have got the wrong end of the stick yet again. They all say that I want to celebrate D-Day by serving spam at street parties. What rubbish! It was Mr Tim Bell who wanted to do that. I merely agreed with him. Which is a very different thing. I have now decided that I am entirely against vulgar publicity stunts on what should be a very solemn occasion. We will celebrate our great victory at D-Day by having spam-fritter street parties, but only in a suitably solemn way.

Tuesday

According to Sir Norma Fowler, who rang me up at 4.30 this morning, we have broken yet another record by having the lowest ever score in the polls. Apparently only 2 per cent of the voters now say they would ever vote Conservative again. "Do you know what time it is, Norma?" I told him in my stern, woken-up-in-the-middle-of-the-night voice. "Yes, you idiot," he replied, "it is time for you to wake up." "But I am awake since you have just woken me," I retorted in a no-nonsense, sharp-as-a-button-even-though-it-is-4.32-in-the-morning-sort of way. "And, anyway," I went on, "this is very good news. Wasn't I behind in the polls last time, and I won a historic victory? Imagine how historic my victory will be this time." At this there was a funny banging sound from down the line, as though someone was hitting his head against the wall many times. Then the line went dead. So I went to the cupboard under the stairs to get out my famous soap box, and practised standing on it in front of the mirror in my dressing gown. "If only the people of Britain could see me now," I thought, "I would win by a landslide."

Wednesday

Today is both a historic and a sad day — i.e. President Nixon has died. In Cabinet I asked for a minute's silence to remember this very great statesman, which was unfortunately spoiled by Mr Waldegrave coming in with a packet of new Eurotunnel Biscuits. "I am sorry," he said, "these are very difficult to open, we may have to wait till next year."

I pointed out that the Americans have this very good idea of calling people President even when they are no longer in power. "You mean it's like us calling you prime minister," said Mr Heseltine, who was doing his Canadian Airforce press-ups in the corner. It was obviously a good-natured joke because everyone laughed. I then pointed out another point about President Nixon which was that, although he had at one time been very considerably unpopular, he was now regarded as a major statesman. "I think we can all take heart from this," I said. "But Mr Nixon first had to resign and then die," said Mr Clarke. Everyone laughed again for some reason, and the result was we did not have our one minute's silence.

Thursday

At last the tide is turning! Jeffrey Archer is convinced that we are going to win in both the local elections and the Euro-elections. He has been on television 17 times in the last two days making his prediction, according to my wife Norman. "And what's more," she told me this morning, "he even sounds as if he believes it."

Unfortunately Mr Portfolio has once again upset the apple cart with one of his speeches, complaining about the long queues in post offices. Of course the queues are long, as stamps are very popular with consumers. And yet the *Daily Telegraph* keeps saying that Mr Portfolio is very clever and one day will be prime minister. As I told my wife Norman: "He is actually not very bright and gets most things wrong." "No wonder you are worried," she said sympathetically.

Friday

Mr Portfolio has made another of his speeches supporting me by disagreeing with all my policies. This time he says he cannot accept the single European currency as it will end British sovereignty. I am sure this is completely untrue as British sovereignty ended ages ago. However I am not 100% certain of this so I will have to consult Miss Hogg. It is her job to know what my policy is on these matters, even before I do!

Saturday

I am becoming in no small measure annoyed by everybody in my party. Mrs Shepherd (who is like Mrs Bottomley except she is not looking for a new job. Yet!) has told the newspapers that eight out of ten Conservative MPs support me. I have done a sum which shows that this means that seventy MPs (approx.) i.e. a considerable number are *against* me and are therefore not my friends. Now, thanks to Mrs Shepherd, everybody knows this! With so-called friends like her, who needs Bastards?

Sunday

I am really becoming not inconsiderably annoyed now. Another MP called Mr Evans has been on the radio saying I should sack a third of my Cabinet. Again I have done a sum and worked out that this means I must get rid of approximately 6¾ people. How can I do that? I can't possibly sack ¾ of Mr Waldegrave, for example. Besides, who will do their jobs if they go? These backbenchers never think anything through, which is why they are not in the Cabinet. And if they were I would sack them. Oh yes.

Thursday

Today was a not entirely satisfactory day for the Conservative Party. According to the papers we have got the fewest votes in a local election since records began. But I am in no measure dispirited. Oh no. Moreover the results were not my fault. They were entirely the fault of Sir Norma Fowler, who is Chairman of the Party (until my friend Jeffrey is ready to take over). "But you said that you were taking personal charge of the campaign, prime minister," said Sir Norma, when I carpeted him. "So I was," I told him, "but you were in charge of the result." That certainly shut him up, particularly when I told him that he would also be in charge of the result of the Euro-elections.

Saturday

Today is another very historic day, as the Channel Tunnel is now open even though it will remain closed until the autumn. My wife Norman and I were invited to travel on the first historic train. "I am sorry," said the guard, "the first carriage is only for heads of state, like President Mitterrand and Mrs Thatcher. You are with the ex-prime ministers such as Mr Heath and Mr Kinnock." It was a very nice journey, although because it was underground you did not get much of a view out of the window. Fortunately I did not feel at all seasick, although some of the journalists seemed to be quite ill in the next carriage. When we arrived in Europe, everyone went off to do some shopping in the local supermarket, which funnily enough is called Sainsbury's, just like in England. On the way back to the train I saw my ex-friend Mr Lamont carrying several plastic bags full of clinking bottles. "Pardon me, boy," he said, "is that the Onanugu choo-choo?" and climbed aboard. He certainly seemed to be in good spirits. When some journalists asked me for a quote, I told them: "Today shows that we are now at the heart of Europe for good, unless I decide that we are not at the next election."

Sunday

The Sunday papers are all saying that I should have a referendum on Europe. This is a very silly idea, as I have said on many occasions. Do they not realise that since my triumph at

Maastricht all this has been settled once and for all? There will be no referendum, unless I decide otherwise, which I might. That is my position and I shall stand firm on it.

Monday

Today I won a great victory over Mr Portfolio when I made him publicly apologise for disagreeing with me over the single European currency. He said he was very sorry indeed, and sat there with his fingers crossed and a smile on his face, laughing repentantly. I will not have to mention him again!

Tuesday

Mr Portfolio has very silly hair, and his name is very silly too. That is why I never think about him.

Wednesday

While I am on the subject of Mr Portfolio, which I wasn't, the newspapers even said that Prince Charles's "back to basics" speech was copied from Mr Portfolio's. This is utter nonsense. His Royal Highness's speech was clearly based on my own — i.e. back to basics, proper spelling, more Shakespeare etc. Perhaps I should not be the one to say it, but Prince Charles has obviously discovered that the key to popularity is to imitate me!

Thursday

Mr Smith has died. It is a very sad day indeed. Everyone is most upset, and at our emergency Cabinet meeting everyone was in tears.

"How tragic that it should have happened now," said Sir Norma Fowler, "just when it looked like Labour might win. How terrible that we've been saved by this appalling stroke of good luck."

"Yes," agreed Mr Clarke, "and it does go to show that you can't rely on anyone with a heart problem." He then gave Mr Heseltine a big smile and a friendly thump on the back.

I then called for a minute's silence as a mark of respect to Mr Smith, and once again Mr Waldegrave spoilt it by bringing in the tea with a big chocolate gateau for Mr Heseltine, which was a present from Mr Portfolio.

"It's not my birthday," said Mr Heseltine, but everyone thought it was a nice gesture all the same.

After the minute's silence which we didn't have, I told the Cabinet that Mr Smith had been a very good friend of mine. "Mr Smith and I", I told them in my special solemn-but-lighthearted voice, "often had a drink together. Sometimes it was tea. And sometimes it was *not* tea. Oh no! It was coffee." They all laughed.

Friday

I am in no small measure amazed at the way everyone is going on about Mr Smith. The newspapers are treating him as though he was the Prime Minister. Which he was not. Nor was he going to be. He was a very nice man, but it must be said that he was a bit dull and obviously could never have taken my job.

To show how true this is, I made a very important and interesting speech today in Scotland, where Mr Smith came from, and as a mark of respect to him the audience observed a ten-minute silence as soon as I had finished.

The best bit of my speech, which was written by me, was Miss Hogg's idea about my beliefs.

"I believe passionately in what I believe," I told the crowd. "I do not believe passionately in what I do not believe. Judge me by what I am. Not what I am not."

At this point, instead of clapping, the audience all sat on their hands, which is obviously a custom in Scotland to show respect to the departed. "He's died!" said one Scotsman. "On his arse!" shouted another for reasons I did not understand.

Anyway, I ended my speech by calling for an end to personal attacks in politics which lower the whole tone of public life.

Saturday

Sir Norma came to see me this morning, having heard my speech. "You're a bloody fool, prime minister," he said. "Without any personal attacks we haven't got anything to put in our manifesto."

He then showed me a booklet with everything crossed out. Only one passage remained. It said: "This man is unfit to hold office. He is weak, ineffectual and has no vision."

"We can't say that," I said. "Yes, we can," Sir Norma replied, giving me a funny look. "But *not* about Mr Smith."

Monday

Today I made a historic speech to launch our campaign to win the Euro-elections. My speech which was entirely my idea, after Miss Hogg had written it out, was very cleverly called "A Resounding No to Europe — But Yes As Well". Though I say it myself, this is one of the most masterly pieces of political brilliance since Mr Heseltine's plan to make us more popular by selling off the Post Office. By saying "No to Europe" I will win all the votes of the people who are against Europe, and then by saying "Yes" we will win all the votes of the people who are in favour of it. When I told the Cabinet that this was our line, they were so impressed that they all jumped out of the window.

Tuesday

My brother Terry hurried over specially from Croydon to tell me that he has discovered a really interesting new fact about our family for his book *"The Authorised History of The Major-Ball Dynasty* by Terry Major-Ball, brother of John Major (the Prime Minister)". He was in the Croydon library doing research into our family tree when he found out that our father Harry Ball-Major was not just an acrobat and maker of garden gnomes, but a very successful farmer in Worcestershire as well. My press officer, Mr Meyer, who came in to check that there was nothing in my brother's book that would look bad in the newspapers, got very excited when he heard this. "This is just what we need to get the shire vote in the Euro-elections. Obviously you've lost the cities, but this might help you hang on to a couple of seats in the country. I can see the headlines now 'Major of Yeoman Stock'..." "Surely Yes-man is more like it?" said my wife Norman, who was brewing up a mug of instant tea for my brother in the micro-wave. She clearly had failed to see the point.

"Yeo is right for you," Terry suggested. "It is half way between yes and no." "You never did have any brains, Terry," I said. "It is just as well you didn't go into politics or you would have been a disaster."

Wednesday

I am getting in no small measure annoyed by all the articles in the newspapers about Mr Blair. Every day there is another one saying how young and dynamic and go-ahead he is, with lots of new ideas for Britain. "No one like that is going to be prime minister," I told Norman.

At least I had one piece of good news today. My ex-friend Mr Lamont has made a very supportive speech saying that the Conservatives have a very good chance of winning the next election. It is a pity he rather spoiled it at the end by saying that this will only happen if we have a new leader. Mr Lamont said in his speech that to beat Mr Blair, the Tories need someone who is mature, silvery-haired, experienced and called Norman. He obviously meant me, since I have all these qualifications, except that he made that silly slip about the name, which shows that he had probably been visiting his friend Mr Onanugu!

Thursday

Mr Hurd has written a very nice note on Foreign Office notepaper, with a delightful new logo reading "F. Off". He tells me that he has decided to lie low during the Euro-election campaign, because he would not wish to take credit for our great victory. "I want there to be no doubt", he wrote, "about who is responsible."

Also in the post came a parcel from my good friend Lord Archer, containing the outline of his latest novel. This is set "some time in the future" when there is a Euro-Election. He describes brilliantly how the Conservatives, under their leader James Colonel, are betrayed by an incompetent party chairman called Sir Herman Disgustinger. But just as the polls are showing that the Tories are going to win no seats at all, Sir Herman falls victim to a terrifying killer-virus called Normanensis fascistitis (Group 4). At this point the hero Godfrey Bowman steps in to take over the chairmanship and the Conservatives win by a huge landslide. Everyone is so impressed that Bowman is invited to become prime minister.

I enjoyed it very much, although the last chapter was rather unconvincing in my judgement.

Friday

Today I travelled to Bristol which is in England to make an important speech for the Euro- elections. As usual, for security reasons, I could not tell anyone I was going, which explained why there was no one at the meeting when I arrived. On the way to the hall we *did* meet somebody who recognised me and shouted: "It's time for you beggars to go!" The policemen with me took him away for some reason, but it gave me a very good idea for my speech, i.e. the most important issue in Britain today is getting beggars off the streets. It is always important for a Prime Minister to listen to the public.

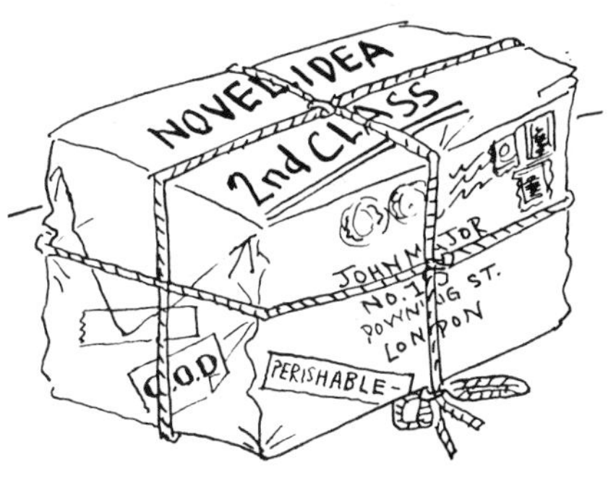

So I promised the good people of Bristol that all the beggars would be taken off the streets. "What will we do with them?" said the one local Conservative man in the audience when it came to asking questions. "There will be a Beggars' Charter," I said, quick as a flash, "and anyone who is bothered by beggars will be able to ring Mr Waldegrave on a special Beggars' Hotline."

Saturday

My beggars speech has been a great success. Everyone is talking about it, even the Bishops! This is very encouraging as one of them, David Shepherd, used to play cricket for England and when I was 15 I swapped his autograph with Terry for that of P.B.H. May, or maybe it was K. Barrington, anyway it was all a long time ago. Oh yes.

Sunday

Everyone is still talking about my beggars speech. The Labour Party have been completely caught on the hop by this. They have come forward with all sorts of new ideas, but not one of them has come up with the Beggars' Charter! No wonder I am Prime Minister and not Mr Blair.

June

Monday

Today was a very historic day 50 years ago. It was D-Day which was the day when Britain first went into the heart of Europe. I thought this was a very good omen for my campaign in the Euro-elections which has exactly the same theme! Mr Meyer tells me that I have to go to a place called Normandy where we are going to have our photographs taken to remember the people who died. Her Majesty the Queen has graciously offered to let me accompany her on her special boat, which is called *Britannia* after the famous song. When I got on board, Her Majesty kindly asked me to get her a stiff gin and "something for the prime minister whom I am expecting". When I explained to her than I was the prime minister, she laughed. "Good heavens," she said, "so you are. How times have changed. The last time I was here it was Mr Churchill. He was a great man." I was very moved to be compared with this great Conservative prime minister. "Oh yes," I said, making a joke, "we shall fight them on the Social Chapter." Unfortunately Her Majesty could not appreciate my joke as she had a sudden attack of sea-sickness.

Tuesday

Today is another historic day as it is the day when all the newspapers have articles about yesterday. But I am not inconsiderably annoyed that they are all showing pictures of Mr Clinton, who was too young even to be born when D-Day happened, unlike me who was considerably alive (i.e. one). I have to say that the French people were very friendly to me when I went for a walkabout in a village called Toutes Directions. All the villagers threw pieces of cheese and shouted, "Monsieur Two-Track à la lanterne!" which Mr Meyer explained showed that they though my opt-out policy was a shining lamp-post in the gloom of Europe.

Wednesday

Today is E-Day-minus-one, i.e. the day before the historic European elections. Sir Norma Fowler has in no small measure cheered me up. "I'm afraid it looks like a landslide, prime minister," he told me. "That is very good news," I said, "it must be as a result of my brilliant election broadcast in which I spelled out my new idea of a two-speed Europe, with ourselves in the fast lane but going slowly."

Sir Norma had obviously not been listening as he interrupted me. "It'll be an anti-Tory landslide, you idiot," he said.

"It is you who are the idiot," I said, quick as a flash. "You cannot even decide what type of landslide it is going to be. And besides, if we are in the fast lane going slowly, the landslide will not hit us. It will hit the car in front, or the one behind."

Thursday

Today I was invited on the famous Today programme, which all politicians have to listen to, to find out what's going on. I was interviewed by the great John Humphrys, who really tried to catch me out over Europe by saying that Mr Gummer and Mr Clarke didn't appear to agree with my new two-track Europe policy, with us driving slowly in the fast lane and everyone hooting behind and flashing their lights. "You are wrong, John," I told him, "my government is entirely united on Europe, whatever the Cabinet may say." He was lost for words and to cover his embarrassment immediately said that it was now time for Mr Rabbi Blue to tell one of his jokes about his granny.

Friday

The newspapers are trying to pretend that we have lost all the by-elections. This is true, but losing five by-elections is not nearly as bad as losing, say, more than five, which I did not. Oh, no. So there. No one is downhearted in this Party and at our Cabinet meeting there were many smiling faces to greet me. Particularly Mr Portfolio, Mr Clarke and Mr Heseltine.

Saturday

Sir Norma came in to warn me again about the Euro-elections. "If we lose, prime minister, it will be due to apathy," he said. "But I've done everything I can. I've made speeches every day," I replied. "That's the trouble," he said, as he tried to strangle me with his bare hands. "Would you like to spend more time with your family again?" I asked him, which seemed to calm him down. Luckily, Mr Meyer came in to help me up from the floor and to tell me about his latest brilliant idea for the Euro-elections. "I have told all the newspapers that if we get one seat it will be a miracle."

Sunday

The miracle has happened! We have won well over the one seat deemed to be miraculous and, in fact, have performed in a manner that could be counted in my judgement as a landslide!! 18 seats is eighteen times as many as one! This is surely a victory in any one's book!

So much for Sir Norma's gloomy predictions. It really is time he went.

I have asked Mr Heseltine if he would like a new job. "Yes, indeed," he said, "when can I move in?" I do not see why Mr Heseltine should want to move into Sir Norma's house, since Sir Norma will be there spending more time with his family. You can see why Mr Heseltine will never be Prime Minister.

Monday

Following our great success in the Euro-elections, when we won 18 times more seats than all the so-called experts predicted, Sir Norma Fowler has decided to rest on his undoubted laurels. When he came to see me this morning he said: "It has always been my intention to resign before you could sack me, prime minister." This was very sad news because it meant that I had to find someone else to take over this very important job of masterminding our victory at the next election. "I am sure you will have lots of phone calls as soon as it is announced that I am giving up," said Sir Norma.

Sure enough, no sooner had he left than the phone rang. It was Mr Heseltine. "I just wanted to let you know, prime minister," he said, "that if you're hoping that I will take on Norma's job, you know what you can do with it. I am, however, prepared to serve you in any way that involves me becoming Prime Minister."

He then put the phone down, and it did not ring again until tea-time. It was my friend Jeffrey Archer. "Prime minister," he said, "I just thought I would offer some advice about the Chairmanship. It is vital that the new man should be in late middle-age, should be popular with the Party workers, an excellent speaker, and should have written a lot of books. Am I making myself clear?"

"Oh, yes," I replied. "You are talking about Douglas. But I cannot move him from the Foreign Office." Jeffrey made a funny snorting noise and rang off.

Tuesday

All the papers are saying that I am planning a reshuffle to give my government an entirely new look. They are saying that I must get tough and wield the axe by sacking such people as Mr Gummer, Mr Waldegrave, Mr Lilley, Mr Portfolio, Mr Patten, Mr Howard, Mr MacGregor, Mrs Bottomley, Mr Clarke, Mr Hurd, Mr Heseltine and someone called Mr Hunt. When I showed the list to my wife Norman, she said: "Haven't you forgotten the most important name of all?" "Oh, yes," I said, "Mr Redwood."

Wednesday

Today, yet again, there are no trains. Millions of people, including Miss Hogg and the man who helps me with my speeches by writing them for me, Mr Morris Norris, have been unable to get to work. Let there be no doubt as to who is to blame, i.e. the trade unions and, in particular, Mr Knapp. My press adviser, Mr Meyer, made a very good point when he said that it was just like the 1970s, when Mrs Thatcher won the election by standing up to the unions. "This could be the chance we've been waiting for, prime minister," he said. "The country is sick and tired of all these strikes." "You are right," I said. "I must be seen to be getting tough. 'Who is running Britain?' That will be our slogan." "So what are you going to do?" asked Mr Meyer. "I shall make it clear that this strike is nothing to do with the Government," I told him.

Thursday

My message has got home, as I heard on the news this morning that the trains are running again. In Mrs Thatcher's day these strikes often went on for weeks. Under my government they only go on for one or two days at a time.

However, I still have one problem, which is to find someone to be the Chairman of the Party.

Jeffrey is being very helpful. He sends me faxes several times a day saying that the job must go to someone who is in the House of Lords and is an extrovert who gives parties for famous people from all walks of life. I think he may have made a mistake here, as Sir David Frost is not yet in the House of Lords — although if he interviews me again, he might well be.

Friday

Today I am flying to a place called Corfu, which is near Greece, for a very important meeting to decide who should be the President of Europe. I would like it to be Sir Leon Brittan, because he would stand up for Britain and show that we are really powerful in the new Europe. Besides, he has been in Brussels for a long time, and he would know how to drive in the fast lane, but slowly. However, Mr Herr Kohl and M. Mitterrand want to have a Belgian called Mr Dehaene who is even fatter than Mr Soames, obviously because he eats so many Belgian chocolates! Mr Hurd and I agreed beforehand that we would not accept Mr Dehaene at any price, because he believes in everyone driving very fast in the fast lane all the time with their lights flashing. We agreed that we would use our veto.

Saturday

Everyone is full of praise for the way I got tough about Mr Dehaene. Britain stands alone, as we did in 1940. Oh yes!

Now, because I have said no, Mr Herr Kohl and M. Mitterrand will have to put someone else forward.

I have made it clear that, whoever is nominated for the job, I will not be dictated to by my European counterparts. That is the job of my backbenchers.

On my return from Corfu, where I got not inconsiderably bitten by mosquitoes, there was a strange message on my answering machine: "I am speaking on behalf of the Queen, President Clinton and the Pope. They all agree that your friend Jeffrey Archer is the best man you could get to be Party Chairman. If he does not get the job, he has told me personally he will join the Labour Party and bring down your Government. His new book of short stories is currently available in all good bookshops."

I spent a not inconsiderable time wondering who this caller could be.

Monday

Everyone is still going on about my great victory in Corfu, when Mr Hurd told me to veto that fat Belgian, Mr Dehaene. There is now no more talk about how I will have to resign. Not that there was before, but now there is even less. In 50 years' time I have no doubt that schoolchildren will be told about my "D-Day" (Dehaene Day) — i.e. the day when I single-handedly took on the might of Germany, under their leader Adolf Kohl, and finally forced them into unconditional surrender!

Tuesday

I do not wish to go on about my historic triumph in Corfu, but when I entered the House of Commons this afternoon, all our people stood up as one and clapped and cheered wildly for several minutes, except Mr Heath. It would be immodest for me to take all the credit for my great achievement, because there were other people involved in the decision, although in the end it was entirely my own.

Wednesday

I don't want to keep mentioning my stupendous triumph in Corfu, but it does seem to have impressed everyone, even the Cabinet. At our meeting today, Mrs Bottomley proposed that they should all sing "For He's A Jolly Good Fellow" and then handed me a note saying "Can I have a new job please?" While Mr Heseltine was telling everyone about his plans to change the red post boxes to facilitate important business mail while phasing out old-fashioned letters, I passed a "hand-delivered" note of my own back to Mrs Bottomley. "You will have to wait till my reshuffle," I told her, "and it would be improper for me at this stage to disclose my intentions with regard to any particular individual, i.e. yourself. Signed in his presence by John Major (Prime Minister)."

July

Thursday

I am glad to say that the thought of my great reshuffle is keeping the Cabinet very much on their toes, oh yes. Let there be no doubt as to who is in charge here, particularly after my historic triumph in Corfu which I do not go on about. This morning several ministers came to see me, obviously hoping that they will not be sacked. Mr Clarke was the first to arrive, saying "I have a brilliant idea for winning the next election, prime minister. We reduce income tax to 5p in the pound before the election is announced and we will win by a landslide." I had to point out to him, as an ex-Chancellor, that there was a not inconsiderable snag to his plan. "That would mean that the Government would very soon run out of money," I said in my financially prudent voice. "Aha," said Mr Clarke, excitedly flicking ash from his cigar all over my biros and my special "Reshuffle Notebook" from Ryman's, "we will then get all the money back by whacking VAT up to 50 percent as soon as we have won the election." Clearly, Mr Clarke must be a front runner for promotion in my reshuffle!

Mr Meyer meanwhile came in with another idea for winning the next election. He suggests that we should put up thousands of posters all over the country showing a picture of Mr Knapp and a lot of trains standing idle, and written underneath: "This is What Britain Would Look Like If There Was A Labour Government."

Friday

I was up all night until half-past nine working on my reshuffle. The way I did it was to put everyone's names on special white cards from Ryman's, and then to match them up with the jobs which I had written on blue cards (also from Ryman's). Eventually, I got everyone matched up, and I was able to draw up my final list which will convince the country that we mean business and that I am now leading a new, dynamic team into the next election.

Firstly, I am to remain as prime minister. Of that there is no doubt! Next, Mr Hurd has very kindly said he will stay on as Foreign Secretary, which is a great relief! Mr Clarke stays at the Treasury, with his brilliant new plan of cutting income tax. Mr Howard keeps the Home Office. Mr Rifkind remains in Defence, Mrs Bottomley will make a superb Health Secretary and the others will all keep their old jobs.

The only post I still have not managed to think of anyone for is that of Party Chairman when Sir Norma Fowler finally goes off to spend less time with me. In the past few days I have received thousands of faxes from loyal party workers, all unanimously putting forward the name of my friend Jeffrey Archer. I noticed that although they were all signed by different people, they all came from the same number: Grantchester 211211 (Jeffax).

Saturday

Today, after reading the faxes, I have decided that there is only one man for the Chairman's job — my friend Jeffrey Archer. Why did I not think of him before?

I was about to ring him when my wife Norman showed me the morning's newspapers.

They said that Mr Archer had been accused of something called "Insider Dealing" which is to do with shares. So now, apparently, he will never be Chairman of the Party. Oh dear. Just when I was going to appoint him. I will obviously have to find someone else.

My press officer, Mr Meyer, tells me I will have to get someone "squeaky clean" this time. Here is my shortlist of possible names:
Cecil Parkinson
Michael Mates
David Mellor
Alan Clark
Norma Lamont
Tim Yeo
Asil Nadir (Mr Mates's friend).

I shall not make up my mind immediately, but I have plenty of time to think about it because I am off on a short holiday to Italy to a place called "G7".

Sunday

G7 is a very nice place not unlike Naples with a big bay and a big mountain with smoke coming out of the top. It is so nice that all the other Heads of State like Mr Clinton and Mr Herr Kohl are here on holiday as well.

We all decided to have a meeting while we were here at which Mr Herr Kohl took me to one side and began to twist my arm behind a pillar. "Stop it. It hurts," I said in my new get-tough statesmanlike voice. Ten minutes later he did. This was after I said I would agree to any fat Belgians or fat Luxemburgers or fat any-other-nationalities that he wanted to make President of the EEC.

Later, our evening meal of pizza and spaghetti was rather ruined when Mr Clinton announced, "Gentlemen, Kim Il Sung is dead."

"Congratulations, you got him at last!" said Mr Yeltsin who was on his fourth bottle of a drink called chianti which looks like Ribena and comes in a funny bottle shaped like the lampstands we have by our beds.

Mr Clinton laughed and I joined in though I did not know what the joke was. Or who Mr Kim Il Sung was.

Monday

This morning we had another meeting, this time about Bosnia. Mr Clinton tells us we have decided to arm the Muslims in order to make the war more fair. "Surely," I whispered to Mr Hurd, "we said we would never give arms to the Muslims?"

"We won't give them," said Mr Hurd, "we'll sell them."

"That's all right, then," I said. "We haven't broken any promises."

Then we flew home from G7 airport where I bought a copy of my friend Jeffrey Archer's new book for Norman. Amazingly, it had already been signed "I am innocent. Best wishes, Lord Archer".

Tuesday (a.m)

I am not going to go on about my triumph in Corfu, but it has to be said that it has completely changed the political climate of our time, oh yes. Since I said no to Mr Dehaene, Mr Herr Kohl has been very considerably more respectful in his dealings with me. Only this morning he sent me a letter saying that we had chosen a Mr Santer from Luxembourg to be President of Europe, instead of Mr Dehaene, and he was sure that I would not be foolish enough to use my veto again. "I know where you live," he added in a rather curious postscript. This is not surprising as it is well known that I live at 10 Downing Street, London, England, Great Britain, the EU, the World, the Solar System, the Universe, SW1 1BF.

Tuesday (p.m.)

Mr Santer has annoyed me in no small measure. He has announced that he is in complete agreement with Mr Dehaene, Mr Delors and Mr Herr Kohl about everything, particularly the Single Currency and the Social Chapter. "What is the meaning of this?" I asked Mr Hurd. "I thought you said he was different?" "So he is, prime minister," replied Mr Hurd. "he is much thinner than Mr Dehaene and spells his name differently." "But what about my great Corfu victory over the federalists?" I asked. "You made your point," said Mr Hurd. "You stood up to Mr Herr Kohl, and now you can afford to be magnanimous by doing what he says."

Wednesday

To complete my regeneration of the Tory Party so that we can win the next election, I am now working on my historic reshuffle. The most important task is finding the right man to be Chairman of the Party. I spent the morning ringing up all the people I could think of, like Mr Heseltine, but they all said that it was far too great an honour for them. Mr Heseltine did, however, come up with one suggestion that I found very flattering, which was that by far the best person to do the job was myself. "And who would do my job in the meantime?" I asked. He laughed in a friendly way, and put the phone down.

Thursday

At last today I had a real stroke of luck with the main bit of my reshuffle. I was in the queue in the tearoom waiting to choose a doughnut from the glass case, when I got chatting to a very nice man who said he had always wanted to meet me because both our fathers had been in the entertainment business. It turned out that we had another thing in common, i.e. that we were both Conservative MPs. Over our cups of tea I suddenly had a brainwave. "Would you like to be Chairman of the Conservative Party?" I asked him. He seemed very surprised and at first said nothing, so I added "and you can also have a job in the Cabinet". He immediately agreed, and offered to buy me a nut slice. It turned out that he was called Mr Hanley, like the famous toy shop, except with an "n" instead of an "m".

After that the rest of my reshuffle was very easy. Mr Hurd, Mr Clarke, Mr Heseltine, Mr Howard, Mr Lilley, Mr Rifkind, Mr Newton and Mr Gummer all stay in the jobs where they have been so successful, as does Mrs Bottomley. Mr Portfolio is to be taught a lesson by giving him his own department. Mr Meyer said that it was a very good "new look" but that I should sack one or two other ministers to show how tough I am. I made out a list of names and then I went off to Ryman's to buy a special box of pins at a summer-reduced rate of £1.99 per 100 (approx), with heads in different colours. I chose a blue one, which I thought was appropriate, and closing my eyes I stuck it in the Daily Telegraph list of the Cabinet. Unfortunately, I found that my first choice to be sacked was myself! Obviously that was impossible, so I tried again and the unlucky names were Mr Brooke, Mr MacGregor and Mr Patten. Also someone called Lord Wakeham whom I had never heard of.

It was the hardest thing I have ever done since I became prime minister, to get Miss Hogg to send them all faxes saying that they had been sacked. Thirty seconds after she had finished, a fax came back from Mr Patten, which said: "It is a great pleasure to be out of your government, you bastard."

Miss Hogg then explained to me that, if I sacked Mr Patten, I would have to promote Mrs Shephard in his place, and give Mr Waldegrave *her* job, whatever it was. "But who then will bring in the tea and biscuits?" I asked. "The Tea and Biscuits portfolio, which is part of the Citizen's Charter and Science brief," Miss Hogg explained, "will have to go

to Mr Hunt, whose job has gone to Mr Portfolio." These reshuffles are certainly very complicated! But you do not get to be prime minister without being able to pick a fresh new team every few months!

Friday

The Labour Party has chosen Mr Blair as its leader. Thank goodness they have picked a man I am not scared of. Oh no. He holds no fears for me!! Just because he is young and has what my wife Norman calls charisma, it does not mean in any way that I am perturbed by him. Quite the opposite, as it happens. In fact I would rather not hear his name mentioned at all so unworried am I by him and I have asked Norman to leave him out of her conversation entirely. Particularly I have asked her to stop saying "I think he's going to win."

Saturday

To show how unfrightened I am by Mr Blair I decided to do what my press officer Mr Meyer said and go to the Test Match with my friend Jeffrey. Jeffrey knows a lot about cricket and gave me a very good tip — i.e. that England would win. They did not, but Jeffrey explained that it was like one of his short stories when the end is always different from the beginning.

It is very nice to see the South Africans playing cricket in England again after so long. This is something we Conservatives can be proud of. "If it had not been for us," I said to a colourful black man called Mr Archbishop Tutu, "the South Africans would not be returning after 29 years."

"No," he said, "we'd have been here ages ago."

He seems to have missed the point like so many church leaders, and not only in *his* country.

Sunday

I am in no small measure looking forward to my holiday as we are going once again to Portugal (I think).

Unfortunately the French air traffic controllers are on strike, which may mean that we will not get there. Why can't other countries get their transport policies in order?

"Shall we go by train instead?" asked Norman, giving me one of her funny looks.

August

Monday

Let there be no doubt that the corner has been turned. As I pointed out to my wife Norman this morning: "Since my great triumph in Corfu, the whole political scene has changed completely out of recognition." "Yes," she replied. "Then Mr Smith was 36 points ahead in the polls, now Mr Blair is 48 points ahead." "No," I patiently explained, in the same voice that I use in the House of Commons when I open my ringbinder and read out what Miss Hogg has told me to say. "Six weeks ago everyone was saying that I was useless. Now they are not saying that any more." "That is because they are on holiday," said Norman in a very unhelpful way. I decided to finish my Fruit-Loops without talking to her.

Tuesday

I am in no small measure considerably annoyed with my brother Terry, who has allowed himself to be made a fool of by writing a book about me just because I am his brother. I have now read the whole book and it is quite obvious that, to sell lots of copies, the publishers have persuaded him to make me out as a very boring person who never did anything interesting until I became prime minister. For example, on page 28, it says that Terry once kicked a football over the fence and broke a pane of glass in Mr Catchpole's greenhouse (our nextdoor neighbour). In fact, it was me who kicked the ball over. Terry was not even there. And, what is more, the ball didn't break anything. Mr Catchpole gave me the ball back, and said: "Try to be more careful in future." I think you will agree that this is a lot more interesting than the way Terry tells the story! When I rang Terry to point this out, he was in a very excitable state and said that he had no time to talk because he was just going down to Croydon to be interviewed on Radio Purley FM by their most famous disc-jockey Kevin Patel. "Be sure to catch it, John," he said. "it is on 89.34KHz and you should be able to pick it up if you take your radio up to the roof and point it in the direction of Purley." Oh dear, it is sad how when an ordinary person suddenly becomes famous, it goes to their head. Before we know it he will be on Desert Island Discs, going on about cricket and embarrassing everybody.

Wednesday

Today Mr Meyer told me that I have to go to a place called

Lithuania, but not for a holiday. Oh no. My work is never done, except when I go on holiday, which is at the end of the week. I could not find Lithuania on my *Daily Telegraph* wall map, but Mr Hurd explained that this was because it used to be in Russia. It is a very small country and not very important, so I was very glad when we came back in the afternoon, after I had had my picture taken with a dull man who is the prime minister. After a while these people all look the same to me!

Thursday

I was very shocked to see on this morning's GMTV (which Norman insists on watching because she likes Eammon and Penny although I prefer Mr Hobday and Mr Humphreys on the wireless, except when they are being rude to Mrs Bottomley, who is only doing her job) that our new Minister of Agriculture Mr Waldegrave has got Mad Cow disease. "Is that what they call BSE?" asked Norman. "No," I said, "that is what people watch the cricket on when it is in the West Indies." When I rang Mr Waldegrave to express my sympathy, he said that it was not him that had the disease but his cows. He has obviously gone completely off his head, imagining that he is a farmer instead of a member of my Cabinet. It is very worrying how quickly this madness spreads. Talking of which, guess who turned up on the GMTV sofa? — my brother Terry. This time he was telling the famous story of the time he borrowed my white plimsolls on a very hot day, and when he came back for tea they were all covered in tar. And I was supposed to have got very cross, which is a complete and utter lie. In fact, he never borrowed the shoes from me since they were his in the first place, and anyway it could not have been tea-time, because I remember that I was up in my room that afternoon looking at my collection of Player's 50 Famous Cricketers cigarette cards. Honestly, if GMTV want an interesting story, they should come to me!

Friday

At last we are on holiday! We flew this morning to our favourite villa in Algarvia, which is near Portugal. It is such a relief to get completely away from politics and the media for two weeks! When we arrived I walked down to the local store which is called Los Tescos, where they have English newspapers, and I was not inconsiderably annoyed to see that all of them had headlines saying Portfolio Lashes Hezza — Big Two Fight It Out. It seems that Mr Portfolio has written a very rude letter to Mr Heseltine, saying that he is not doing his job properly. I immediately bought all the papers and took them back to show Norman, who was sitting by the pool reading Terry's book and laughing out loud. "I like this picture of your pet squirrel Cyril taken in 1955," she said. "It was not my squirrel, it was Terry's," I pointed out, "and anyway it was not called Cyril, it was called Robert." "And what is more," I said, "now is not a time to laugh. Look what these two are doing at home, as soon as my back is turned. Why are they fighting each other?" "Over who is to lead the Party," said Norman. "That is silly," I told her, "when I am already the leader of the Party." Then we went to the local taverna for a glass of their beer, which is called Oranjeboom.

Monday

Villa Del Golfo, Algarve

It is very pleasant to be on holiday in the European Union, whatever the so-called Eurosceptics like Mr Portfolio may think! For a start it only takes 40 minutes on foot from our villa to the local shop, Los Tescos, where you can buy almost everything that you can get at home, such as Golden Grahams, Tetley tea bags and my wife Norman's new favourite Mars Bar Ice Creams, which unfortunately melted before we could get them home, due to the fact that the temperature here in Algarvia is 19 degrees or do I mean 91° in the shade, although there is not much shade! Norman has bought a special sunhat called a sombrero, after reading an article by Libby Purves in the very interesting in-flight magazine they gave us on the aeroplane. "Without a hat," she said, "people go soft in the head. Not that you will need one."

Tuesday

I was just settling down by the pool with my copy of the 1955 Wisden, which was presented to me by the famous composer Sir Tim Rice, when our maid Latima came out to say that I was wanted very urgently on the phone from London. I had to break off reading a not inconsiderably interesting account of the famous Headingley test match when F.S. Trueman (whom I have now met!) took three Pakistani wickets before lunch, to take the call in our bedroom. To my intense annoyance, it was not Miss Hogg to bring me up to date on the new inflation figures, but a Mr Chris Cropper from the *Sutton and Cheam Herald* who wanted me to comment on my brother Terry's book, now that it has apparently become a best-seller. "Terry is the talk of the town," he told me. "You must be very proud of him. What is it like to have a brother who is a star?" "I think you should address that question to Terence," I replied, in the special putting-down voice I am practising to use in the autumn when Mr Blair thinks he will be able to catch me out. But he will not. Oh no.

As soon as I had got back to my sun-lounger and got myself into a comfy position, Latima came out again. "Telefono," she said, which I knew from my Portuguese-in-10-Minutes phrasebook meant "the telephone". This time it was a Mr Dave Pritt of Radio Cambridgeshire's Good Morning Fenland Show, who said: "And now we've got Terry's brother John live from his holiday retreat in the Algarve, who will be telling us more about Terry's book after we've heard Simon and Garfunkel's The Sound of Silence." At this, loud music began to play for a not inconsiderable amount of time, and I was kept waiting. Finally, Mr Pritt came back on and said, "Hi, John, what's it like having a brother who's a star?" Luckily, I had my reply ready and I told him: "I refer you to the answer I gave earlier to the previous questioner." That shut him up!

Wednesday

I was enjoying a well-earned afternoon nap by our pool, when once again our maid Latima appeared shouting "Terryphone, Terryphone". "No," I told her, in a special kindly but firm voice like when I am explaining why Mrs Bottomley is quite right to close down all the hospitals, "in England we say 'telephone' with an 'l'." "OK, si, señor," she said. "Your brother Telly phone." When I had got up to the bedroom, sure enough, it was my brother sounding a bit like he does after Christmas dinner, when he's had one too many of the Bailey's Irish Creams. "Hullo, John," he said, "guess who?" "I know only too well who it is," I replied in a not inconsiderably frosty manner. He went on: "I am ringing on one of these new mobile telephone things. Have you seen them? You can ring people up from parties, like I'm doing now. I'm at this party in Chelsea." "What do you want?" I said somewhat impatiently. "Because I am very busy having my holiday." "This girl I am with wants to say something to you," he said. "She says her mother has always voted Conservative." At this point a woman's voice broke in, rather fuzzily, saying: "Are you really Terry's brother? You must be ever so proud of him. He's so sexy." At this she giggled and rang off, and I had to tell Latima that if anybody called Terry phoned again she was to say that I was in no small measure out.

Thursday

Today I managed to borrow a copy of last Sunday's *Sunday Times* from the people staying next door who have come to Algarvia to play golf. He is a retired businessman who used to make lawn-mowers. "Excuse me saying so," he said, "but you look a bit like that twit they got in after they'd booted out dear old Maggie. I don't know why they don't give the job to his brother. My wife's reading his book. She says it's the best laugh she's had in years. In bed last night she read me this bit about Cyril the Squirrel eating all the Marmite sandwiches." "It was not called Cyril," I told him firmly, "its name was Robert. And besides, the sandwiches were chocolate spread, not Marmite. How many times do I have to correct all Terry's ridiculous mistakes?" The man gave me a very funny look and said: "If I were you, old boy, I'd wear a hat in this heat," and drove off in his golf cart. But fortunately he left me several bits of the *Sunday Times* so that I could catch up with what had been happening in England while we had been away. The most important thing is that Mr Portfolio has really put his foot in it again. He is putting a lot of disabled people out of work and is blaming it all on the EC. As I explained to my wife Norman: "The interesting thing is that the person responsible for signing the European directive in question, No.93/36, was none other than the Chief Secretary to the Treasury, ie

Mr Cleverdick Portfolio himself." "I wouldn't worry about Mr Portfolio," she said, "not while you're on holiday." "I am not in any manner of shape or form worried by Mr Portfolio's attempts to grab the headlines while I am away," I told her. "Mr Portfolio isn't grabbing the headlines," she said, holding up the cover of the Culture'n' Lifestyle Section of the *Sunday Times*. "it is your brother. Look what it says: 'El Tel is Numero Uno, Reckons TV's Mariella'."

Friday

I was just in the middle of doing my 10 lengths in the pool, which I do every day after breakfast as a way of keeping fit, when Latima again disturbed me, calling out: "Ees Ingleterry on ze phone." This was the final straw. Running upstairs still dripping wet, I shouted into the telephone: "You are not to ring again on any account. I have had quite enough of you and your so-called success." "I'm sorry, Prime Minister," said a lady's voice, which I recognised to my surprise as being that of Miss Hogg. "I just wanted to let you know that since you've been away everything has been going brilliantly. Inflation is down, the stock market is soaring, unemployment is down for the 6th consecutive month and 'A' Levels have broken all records. And, just to cap it all, as an added bonus, your brother Terry is completely flavour of the month, the most popular man in town. Who knows, some of it may rub off on you!" I am glad to say I managed to keep my temper and threw the telephone into the pool.